CONTENTS

Ships in Focus Publications

Correspondence and editorial:
Roy Fenton
18 Durrington Avenue
London SW20 8NT
020 8879 3527
rfenton@rfenton.demon.co.uk
Orders and photographic:
John & Marion Clarkson
18 Franklands, Longton
Preston PR4 5PD
01772 612855
sales@shipsinfocus.co.uk
© 2001 Individual contributors,
John Clarkson and Roy Fenton.

Printed by Amadeus Press Ltd., Cleckheaton, Yorkshire. Designed by Hugh Smallwood, John Clarkson and Roy Fenton.
SHIPS IN FOCUS RECORD
ISBN 1 901703 13 4

SHIPS IN FOCUS 1

This issue has a strong marine engineerin specific types of steam or diesel engine engineering ancestor. Readers more fam than the inside will find they are not neglec..u, ..uwever, and we include the usual quota of photographs and ships' histories, including every vessel fitted with the three less successful types of machinery. We are helped in this because *Record* 16 has the bonus of eight extra pages, included to allow four pages to be devoted to the index to *Records* 13 to 16. However, we would encourage every *Record* reader not to neglect the consideration of what made ships go. Although we all read journals like this for pleasure, the editors believe the enjoyment of any hobby can be enhanced by a deeper understanding of the reasons things were made the way they were. Editing the contributions on the North Eastern Marine reheated engine, for instance, was a salutary lesson that not all triple-expansion engines were the same. Back in *Record* 9, explaining the differences between these engines was the challenge we threw down to marine engineers who had asked us to include more details of a ship's machinery.

As an experiment, the next issue of *Record* will include a colour section. With our photographic content largely originating before colour photography was commonplace, our limitation to black and white has not been a major constraint. However, there are occasional subjects we wish to cover to which only colour can do justice. Whether colour sections become a regular feature depends on extra sales covering the additional cost.

Mention of cost provides a cue to bring up subscriptions, many of which fall due for renewal following this issue. Here too we can offer good news, as we are offering significant savings to those prepared to take out extended subscriptions (see below). For instance, any UK reader taking out a nine-issue subscription will be getting *Record* post free, whilst non-UK readers will also be making a substantial saving. Please consider taking out one of these extended subscriptions; you will be helping us to reduce our administrative burden, and will be making sure that what many readers tell us is their favourite shipping journal arrives on your doormat regularly just as soon as it is published. And you will qualify for discounts, such as that on our latest book advertised opposite.

John Clarkson
Roy Fenton

April 2001

SUBSCRIPTION RATES FOR RECORD

Subscribers make a saving on the postage of three issues, and receive each *Record* just as soon as it is published. They are also eligible for concessions on newly-published *Ships in Focus* titles. Readers can start their subscription with *any* issue, and are welcome to backdate it to receive previous issues.

	3 issues	6 issues	9 issues
UK	£23	£44	£63
Europe (airmail)	£25	£47	£68
Rest of world (surface mail)	£25	£47	£68
Rest of world (airmail)	£30	£56	£81

Harrison's *Statesman* of 1895, first of 22 classic four masted cargo liners. See page 194. *[George Scott collection]*

Fleet in Focus
HARRISONS' FOUR MASTERS
Stephen Howells

THE PIONEERS
STATESMAN (above, left and opposite left)
Workman, Clark and Co. Ltd., Belfast; 1895, 6,153gt, 450 feet
T. 3-cyl. by Workman, Clark and Co. Ltd., Belfast

The 22 four-masters built for Harrison Line between 1895 and 1921 were one of the classic groups of cargo liners, instantly recognisable because of their rig and their enormous natural-draft funnels. This is an appropriate, if sad, time to illustrate the group as their owners - one of the few great survivors of British shipping - announced late last year that they were transferring their remaining liner shipping operations to P&O, although their joint venture with Bibby continues to manage a number of bulk carriers.

Statesman, second of the name and the first of the initial pair of four-masters, is seen above at Montreal in 1915, with a floating crane alongside loading motor launches. These are seen again in the deck view on the opposite page: note the timber screens which have been erected along her decks.

Statesman met her end at the hands of *UB 43* in the Mediterranean on 3rd November 1916, by when she was quite an elderly lady. Even after receiving several shells and torpedoes she did not sink for two days after she had been abandoned. With the exception of six lost in the attack, the *Statesman's* complement

was landed at Malta by a Royal Navy vessel. *[NMM P17014 and N47700]*

CRAFTSMAN (opposite page right and bottom)
Charles Connell and Co., Glasgow; 1897, 6,196gt, 450 feet
T. 3-cyl. by Dunsmuir and Jackson, Glasgow

Compared with previous Harrison vessels, the four-masters represented a quantum leap upwards in tonnage, being almost a third larger than their previous biggest, the *Barrister* of 1893 and her sisters. The

scholarly work on Harrison Line by economic historian F.E. Hyde sheds some light on this brave move. It seems that one of the Harrison Line partners, John W. Hughes, applied mathematical principles based on actuarial practice to help the company decide on its investment policy. In 1893, Hughes' figures showed that the bigger ship costing £70,000 (compared with £53,000 for *Barrister*) would return a satisfactory annual income of £7,000 over an expected life of 20 years as her running costs per ton of cargo carried were lower than for the smaller ship. Professor Hyde

goes on to analyse running costs which show that Hughes was correct for what were called 'Class 1' ships in the years up to 1914.

Indeed, *Craftsman* went on proving useful for much longer than her designed 20 years, and was one of four of the group which ended their days in the whaling business, their size making them well suited for conversion to factory ships. The rebuilding of *Craftsman* as *Ernesto Tornquist* has already been covered in *Record* 5, page 43 which describes how she worked under Argentine ownership, latterly as a tanker, until wrecked on South Georgia whilst arriving with stores and personnel from Norway on 15th October 1950. At 53 she was the longest-lived of the four masters.

Craftsman is seen, bottom, as a transport (probably during the Boer War) with the number 124 and a large awning over her bridge. This photograph shows a different layout to her predecessor *Statesman*, with the bridge moved forward of the second mast. The view on deck (below) shows an officer supervising the lascar crew swinging out one of her boats. *[NMM P16898 and N47821]*

WORKMAN

Workman, Clark and Co. Ltd., Belfast; 1898, 6,116gt, 450 feet
T. 3-cyl. by Workman, Clark and Co. Ltd., Belfast
The third four master, similar in size to *Statesman* and *Craftsman*, was *Workman* (an appropriate name in view of her builders) which had a very short career, wrecked south of Rio de Janeiro on Boxing Day 1912 whilst on the long haul from the west coast of North America to London. For completeness, the ship is included here although no photograph has been found.

461-FOOT DESIGN
HISTORIAN (opposite)
Harland and Wolff Ltd., Belfast; 1896, 6,857gt, 461 feet
T. 3-cyl. by Harland and Wolff Ltd., Belfast

The four-masted design was rethought several times over the quarter century during which they were constructed, and the one-off *Historian* (second of the name) lost the long bridge deck of the *Statesman* and *Craftsman*. She was the second of the four-masters to be delivered, but to highlight the differences and to show the development of the design, the ships are illustrated here by group, rather than by strict order of build. *Historian* is seen in a US port.

    Historian's post-Harrison career saw her trading from 1922 to 1925 as *Arabestan* for Hajee Nemazee of Hong Kong who operated a fleet of pilgrim ships (see *Record* 11, page 154). She saw out her final days in Italian ownership, Industrie Navali Societa Anonima of Genoa first naming her *Delia*. They then tripled the name they first thought of, and she became *Delia Terzo*. These owners sent her to be broken up at Savona in 1931. [*Mariners Museum PB3696 courtesy Peter Newall*]

COLLEGIAN CLASS
COLLEGIAN (this page)
Charles Connell and Co., Glasgow; 1899, 7,236gt, 470 feet
T. 3-cyl. by Dunsmuir and Jackson, Glasgow

Collegian was the lead ship of a batch of five, following on immediately from the *Statesman* group with some detail changes, such as extra-long derricks at the second mast (seen particularly well in the deck view), and 10 feet extra length. The lower view shows the framework for the awning over the bridge, and appears to be a wartime view: the paintwork appears grey and the boats are swung out.

    Collegian herself was a First World War loss, like *Statesman* attacked in the Mediterranean whilst on Harrison's Liverpool to Calcutta service. The protagonist was *UB 48* and the date 20th October 1917. [*NMM P16889 and N47896*]

POLITICIAN (right)

C.S. Swan and Hunter Ltd., Newcastle-on-Tyne; 1899, 7,228gt, 470 feet
T. 3-cyl. by the Wallsend Slipway and Engine Co. Ltd., Wallsend-on-Tyne

Sold by Harrisons in 1922, conversion for whaling greatly extended the life of the former *Politician*. As described and illustrated in *Record* 5, page 44, she became Salvesen's *Coronda* in 1922. After war damage sustained in September 1940 her career became sedentary, serving as a base ship until in June 1946 she was broken up at Ghent by Van Heyghen Frères.

    Politician is also seen at a US port, probably loading cotton from the huge but somewhat unsteady looking warehouse. Detail study of this class show numerous detail differences, including the number of boats and position of the crow's nest. *[World Ship Photo Library, courtesy George Scott]*

TACTICIAN (above)

C.S. Swan and Hunter Ltd., Newcastle-on-Tyne; 1900, 7,281gt, 470 feet
T. 3-cyl. by the Wallsend Slipway and Engine Co. Ltd., Wallsend-on-Tyne

The four-masters were particularly useful ships for the service between Liverpool and New Orleans and other ports in the Gulf of Mexico, which Harrisons had inaugurated in 1866, soon after the American Civil War. Their capacity matched the huge cargoes of cotton which were available during the season, and which were packed into their holds by 'screwmen'. Outside the season, the big ships were usually employed on Harrison's service to Calcutta.

    Tactician was sold for £20,000 in 1922, and gave Japanese owners 13 years' service as *Yojin Maru* before broken up in Kobe. *[Captain J.F. van Puyvelde]*

PATRICIAN (opposite top)

C.S. Swan and Hunter Ltd., Newcastle-on-Tyne; 1901, 7,474gt, 470 feet
T. 3-cyl. by the Wallsend Slipway and Engine Co. Ltd., Wallsend-on-Tyne

Seen in Liverpool on 17th May 1914, *Patrician* was another to end her days in whaling, but arrived there by a roundabout and rather unusual route. In 1914 the Admiralty decided to modify merchant ships to resemble battleships presumably in an attempt to confuse spies and passing Zeppelins about the whereabouts of the Grand Fleet. *Patrician* became a double for HMS *Invincible*, at least until the folly of tying up large and useful cargo carriers was belatedly realised. But once Their Lordships had their hands on *Patrician* they were reluctant to let her go, and in 1915 they had her rebuilt as a tanker, becoming *Teakol*, later *Vineleaf* and on

returning to civilian life, *British Vine*. In 1923 she was sold to Norwegians and as *Busen* worked in the Antarctic with two catchers, *Busen 1* and *Busen 2*, flensing the whales until she was full and then returning to Europe. *Busen* was broken up at Genoa in 1935. *[F.W. Hawks, courtesy Peter Newall]*

YEOMAN

Charles Connell and Co., Glasgow; 1901, 7,379, 470 feet
T. 3-cyl. by Dunsmuir and Jackson Ltd., Glasgow

Harrison's names are often described as being those of 'occupations', but a number fell outside this strict definition with, for instance, *Patrician* denoting a status in society. It was logical to follow this ship with *Plebian*, and in fact her sister was launched under this name. But between

July and September 1901 the company recoiled at the prospect of a stately cargo ship belonging to a respectable line recalling the lower classes of Ancient Greece, and the name *Yeoman* was substituted.

Alas, *Yeoman* was to be the shortest-lived of the four-masters, and when under three years old, on 10th February 1904, she was wrecked near Corunna whilst on a voyage from Liverpool to Calcutta. Five lives were lost and Harrisons did not use this fine name again.

Rather than use underwriters, the company had their own insurance fund, and 1904 proved a bad year for this as, besides the loss of over £100,000 on the *Yeoman* and her cargo, the *Inventor* (2,291/1878) collided with and sank Strick's *Goolistan* (2,756/1898) off Portugal on 10th September. Probably in view of her very short life, no photograph has been found of *Yeoman*.

CIVILIAN (above)
Charles Connell and Co., Glasgow; 1902, 7,100gt, 470 feet
T. 3-cyl. by Dunsmuir and Jackson, Glasgow
Externally, *Civilian* appears to be a development of the *Collegian* group, with a much extended forecastle and bridge deck.

She was to be yet another Harrison war loss whilst sailing through the Mediterranean to Calcutta, being torpedoed by *UC 74* on 6th October 1917 and sinking with the loss of two lives.
[Peter Newall collection]

TWIN SCREWS
MECHANICIAN

Workman, Clark and Co. Ltd., Belfast; 1900, 9,044gt, 482 feet

T. 6-cyl. by Workman, Clark and Co. Ltd., Belfast

Further increases in size were accompanied by the adoption of twin screws for three ships. In contrast to the others, which were employed in the Calcutta trade in the off-season for cotton, the twin-screw ships were usually kept on the Gulf of Mexico service all year round, carrying lumber, grain, molasses, cotton seed, oil and meal. The top photograph, however, shows *Mechanician* as a wartime horse or mule transport; note the stalls on deck and the canvas wind sails intended to increase air flow to her holds.

Perhaps her twin screws and 12 knots attracted *Mechanician* to the Royal Navy, and she is described as becoming 'an armed escort vessel' in 1917. However, it was whilst carrying Government stores that she was lost on 20th January 1918 when torpedoed by *UB 35* in the English Channel west of St. Catherines Point with the loss of 13 of her crew. The two lower photographs show her gradually disappearing. *[NMM P16988, P16989, and P16990]*

CUSTODIAN (top and middle) and
POLCEVERA (bottom)
*Charles Connell and Co., Glasgow; 1900,
9,214gt, 482 feet*
*T. 6-cyl. by Dunsmuir and Jackson,
Glasgow*

Custodian almost suffered the same fate as her near-sister *Mechanician* on 20th March 1918 when torpedoed in the Irish Sea. Although three lives were lost, the ship was saved by beaching in Belfast Lough, and *Custodian* lived to fight another war. This would have been her third, as in the top photograph, with soldiers on deck and painted hull number, she is a Boer War transport.

Custodian was sold for £35,000 to Henry Giffin of Cardiff in 1923 and named *Polcevera*, but this was just a preliminary to her becoming a whaling ship, and the bottom photo may well show her laid up. In 1926 she was fitted with a stern ramp and lost two of her masts to become *N.T. Nielsen-Alonso*, as illustrated in *Record* 5, page 44. New owners were Hvalfangerselskab Polaris A/S, and managers Melsom & Melsom of Larvik. For her first five whaling seasons she was based in Hobart, Tasmania, but from 1931 she worked from Larvik.

N.T. Nielsen-Alonso escaped the German occupation, but not the force of German arms. On 22nd February 1943, whilst bound from Glasgow to New York in convoy ON 166, she was hit by torpedoes from both *U 92* and *U 573* in position 48 north by 31.24 west, killing three of the 53 crew. Not for the first time, torpedoes failed to sink the former four-master, and an escort vessel had to finish the job. *[Top: NMM P16900; middle: George Scott collection; bottom: A. Duncan, courtesy Peter Newall]*

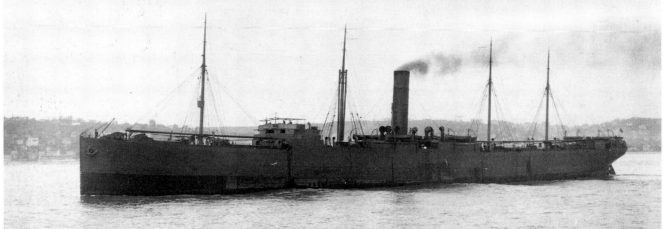

WAYFARER (this page)
Workman, Clark and Co. Ltd., Belfast; 1903, 9,599gt, 505 feet
T. 6-cyl. by Workman, Clark and Co. Ltd., Belfast
Breaking strict chronology again, we show *Wayfarer*, the third and last twin-screw ship Harrisons built, and indeed their longest vessel until 1971. The photograph in camouflage paint was taken at Galveston on 7th December 1918, the flags possibly being a belated celebration of the armistice.

Her post-Harrison career was unusual in that she was sold in 1923 to a United States owner, Robert Dollar of San Francisco, who by then would have a choice of reasonably-priced US war-built tonnage. She was renamed *Virginia Dollar* under the Hong Kong flag for only two years, then becoming *Angiolina R* and later *Susa* under the Italian flag. In 1932 she was laid up at Genoa and subsequently demolished there. *[Middle: NMM P17038, bottom P17039]*

THE HUNTSMAN GROUP
HUNTSMAN (1)
Charles Connell and Co. Ltd., Glasgow; 1904, 7,460gt, 470 feet
T. 3-cyl. by Dunsmuir and Jackson Ltd., Glasgow
The first *Huntsman* was yet another victim of a German submarine whilst on a voyage from Liverpool to Calcutta, but this time in the Atlantic, 180 miles off Fastnet. The date was 25th

February 1917 and the U-boat *U 50*. There were two casualties. No photograph has been found of this *Huntsman*.

INVENTOR (opposite top)
D. and W. Henderson and Co. Ltd., Glasgow; 1910, 7,679gt, 470 feet
Q. 4-cyl. by D. and W. Henderson and Co. Ltd., Glasgow
After a gap of six years during which Harrison concentrated on building smaller Class 2 and Class 3 ships, the *Huntsman* design was perpetuated with the company taking delivery of four ships from 1910 to 1912.

Inventor was the first four-

master to see her full intended life out under Harrison ownership, being broken up at Genoa in 1932. *[Glasgow University Archives DC101/1229]*

EXPLORER (opposite bottom)
Charles Connell and Co. Ltd., Glasgow; 1910, 7,608gt, 470 feet
Q. 4-cyl. by Dunsmuir and Jackson Ltd., Glasgow
Explorer's career ran in parallel with that of *Inventor* completed just a month earlier, both ships ending up in a Genoese scrapyard in June 1932. They were just two of the ten ships Harrisons sold for scrap in that dismal year for shipping.

BOTANIST (above)
D. and W. Henderson and Co. Ltd.,
Glasgow; 1912, 7,688gt, 470 feet
Q. 4-cyl. by D. and W. Henderson and Co.
Ltd., Glasgow
One disadvantage of the four-masted rig
was removing all those topmasts when
visiting Manchester, as *Botanist's* crew
have clearly had to do. Also interesting in
this photograph is the boom for the
paravane, present although *Botanist* is in
peace-time colours.
Homeward bound from Calcutta on 25th
March 1920, *Botanist* was making a call at
Colombo when she hit a reef on the east
coast of Ceylon. Abandoned five days
later, she became a constructive total loss.
[Peter Newall collection]

DIPLOMAT (1)
Charles Connell and Co. Ltd., Glasgow; 1904, 7,615gt, 470 feet
T. 3-cyl. by Dunsmuir and Jackson, Glasgow
Diplomat had the dubious distinction of being the first four-master lost by enemy action. On the inevitable voyage from Calcutta to the United Kingdom, on 13th September 1914 she was captured and sunk by SMS *Emden*, during a cruise in which the German light cruiser was to account for 22 ships.

The *Emden* seems to have robbed *Diplomat* of the opportunity of surviving to be photographed. Readers' help is earnestly requested in finding shots of her and the other missing four masters

LAST OF THE BREED
DEFENDER (opposite middle and bottom)
Charles Connell and Co. Ltd., Glasgow; 1915, 8,078gt, 482 feet

Q. 4-cyl. by Dunsmuir and Jackson Ltd., Glasgow
Defender represented a modest increase in size over the previous ships of the *Huntsman* group, but retained the same layout of decks and masts. Apart from representing what was undoubtedly the zenith of the design, originally developed 20 years earlier, her claim to fame is that she was to become the very last survivor of the group. She arrived at Barrow on 8th June 1952 for breaking up by T.W. Ward Ltd. after 37 years and the best part of two wars in Harrison ownership, outliving even the whale ship conversions.

Defender lived up to her name: she survived a torpedo attack by *UB 64* off Cork on 24th July 1917. Further evidence of the group's ability to absorb battle damage was her living through the Luftwaffe attack on Bari on 2nd December 1943, in which exploding ammunition ships added to the

destruction. *[Opposite middle: NMM P16907; bottom: A. Duncan]*

ASTRONOMER (both above)
D. and W. Henderson and Co. Ltd., Glasgow; 1917, 8,681gt, 482 feet
Q. 4-cyl. by D. and W. Henderson and Co. Ltd., Glasgow
It was the classic profile of *Astronomer* in the lower of the two photographs above which led to the author's interest in the Harrison four-masters.

Alas, the ship herself was an early war loss. *Astronomer* was torpedoed by *U 58* on 1st June 1940 whilst carrying naval stores from Rosyth to Scapa Flow, sinking the next day with the loss of four of her crew of 55. Fortunately, the 52 naval ratings on board survived this encounter with the enemy. *[Upper: A. Duncan]*

DIPLOMAT (2) (both above)
Charles Connell and Co. Ltd., Glasgow;
1921, 8,240gt, 482 feet
Two steam turbines by Dunsmuir and
Jackson Ltd., Glasgow
Diplomat and her sister *Huntsman (2)* were
part of Harrison's brief flirtation with steam
turbines - another was the *Dramatist*
(5,443/1920) - an experience which set
them against specifying this form of
machinery in newbuildings until after the
Second World War, and even then quickly
moving on to motorships.

This last chapter of the story of
the four-masters is the familiarly
depressing one of losses during the
prolonged and appallingly costly Battle of
the Atlantic. On 27th November 1940,
whilst on a voyage from New Orleans to
Liverpool, *Diplomat* was sunk off Ireland by
a submarine believed to have been *U 104*.
The doubt arises because the submarine
itself was lost before it could return to
base and confirm its victims. *[Lower: A.
Duncan]*

HUNTSMAN (2) (both above)
Charles Connell and Co. Ltd., Glasgow;
1921, 8,196gt, 482 feet
Two steam turbines by Dunsmuir and
Jackson Ltd., Glasgow
Huntsman was not only the last of the four-masters to be completed, she was almost certainly the most expensive at £4,000,000 - a price inflated by the shortage of shipbuilding capacity following the First World War and disruption in the ship yards. The owners' chagrin at such a price can be imagined as, by the time *Huntsman* was delivered, the line was already laying ships up, such had trade on their routes declined since 1914.

Huntsman was an early and celebrated war loss, captured in the South Atlantic by the *Graf Spee* on 10th October 1939 and later sunk. Four of her officers were taken on board the German heavy cruiser, and remained there during the Battle of the River Plate, being released when *Graf Spee* put into Montevideo. The remainder of the crew also had an adventurous time, being transferred to the supply ship *Altmark*. When *Altmark* sought refuge in a Norwegian fjord, the crew were released by HMS *Cossack*, whose captain turned a blind eye to the vexed question of Norwegian neutrality. *[Lower: World Ship Photo Library]*

Not until the 1960s did Harrisons build further ships matching the dimensions of the four-masters, although they did renew their fleet during the interwar years, taking advantage of good cheap ships coming on the market and shipyards desperate for work at any price. It can only be concluded that, in the deeply depressed trading which persisted right up to 1939, the company did not feel confident about filling further big ships. A major factor was the company's loss to the United States Shipping Board of much of the cotton out of New Orleans and Gulf ports, a trade for which the big cargo carriers were eminently suited.

As a personal conclusion from one who never saw any of the vessels (unless, as a toddler being taken on a Mersey ferry, I unknowingly witnessed one of the last sailings of the *Defender*) these vessels must vie with some of the better Blue Funnel designs for the title of the most handsome cargo liners ever built. And, judging by their ability to absorb damage, their adaptability and longevity, they were as well designed and built as they looked.

THE MACLAGAN DIESEL
David Burrell

Swan, Hunter and Wigham Richardson Ltd., formed by amalgamation in 1903, were the centre of a group of companies which included Wallsend Slipway and Engineering Co. Ltd., North of Ireland Shipbuilding Co. Ltd. and others. In 1913 they acquired Barclay, Curle and Co. Ltd. who brought with them the North British Diesel Engine Works.

Both Swan Hunter and Barclay Curle were early pioneers in the British diesel field. Swan Hunter built the first British seagoing motorship, the Laker *Toiler* (1,659/1910) powered by a Polar diesel (see *Record* 12, page 249). Barclay, Curle built and engined *Jutlandia* (4,874/1912) for the East Asiatic Co., Copenhagen, a sister of *Selandia* (4,950/1912) and the third ship in the series. For her Barclay, Curle built Burmeister & Wain type engines.

Whilst many British shipbuilders and marine engineers developed in-house diesels only one succeeded, the Doxford. The others fell by the roadside by 1945, replaced by licence-built Doxfords or European marques, in the main Burmeister & Wain and Sulzer. After the First World War, Swan Hunter developed the Neptune range of diesels, and the North British Engine Works built their own four-stroke, single-acting diesel which, in 1921-3, went into six Barclay, Curle ships, five for British India and one for the Union Steamship Co. of New Zealand Ltd.

With the aim of producing more power, North British - in common with others - turned their attention to a double-acting diesel, designed by J.C.M. Maclagan, which was to prove a spectacular failure when fitted in three Barclay, Curle built ships. The shipping press of the period largely limited itself to fulsome praise, rarely hinting at failure, but evidence for this comes from company archives. A working model was exhibited on the Swan Hunter stand in the Palace of Engineering at the 1924 British Empire Exhibition, along with a model of *Swanley*, the first ship fitted with a Maclagan.

Motor Ship described the Maclagan as 'A radical departure from all existing ideas in Diesel-engine construction...' Lloyd's Register Ship and Engineer Surveyor John Guthrie, when writing *A History of Marine Engineering*, included it in the opposed piston section, not because it fitted but because '...it defies classifying into any other category.' Dennis Griffiths, in his paper 'The British crosshead marine diesel engine between the wars' wrote 'Maclagan adopted a very logical approach to the problem of combustion effects on the lower piston rod and gland; he eliminated them.'

There was a single, long piston in a cylinder made in two lengths coupled by tie rods. Top and bottom stationery cylinder heads were secured to the engine frames and the cylinder oscillated between them. The long piston had outside gudgeon pins midlength protruding through the opening between the two halves of the liner and engaged fork end bearings of a connecting rod on the crank. The crosshead, through linkage and levers, passed the reciprocating motion to the cylinder liners which reciprocated in phase with the piston, but on a shorter stroke. Each liner had exhaust ports uncovered by the piston and scavenge ports uncovered by the movement of the liner.

Seen here when new, Harris and Dixon's *Swanley* was the first recipient of a MacLagan diesel, but in three years it had to be replaced. In 1932 she became *Hoperange* (see page 210) and in 1937 was sold to Norway and renamed *Hird*. Arriving at Dunkirk on 8th May 1940 she was still there when the Allied evacuation started. On 28th May she sailed with nearly 4,000 personnel, stopping to pick up more from the sinking destroyer HMS *Wakeful* in the English Channel. Her end came on 15th September 1940 when, on a voyage from Panama City and Mobile for Manchester and straggling from convoy HX72, she was torpedoed by *U 65*. Her crew were picked up by the Icelandic trawler *Thorofur* and landed at Fleetwood. *[Glasgow University Archives UGD 136/2/1/40]*

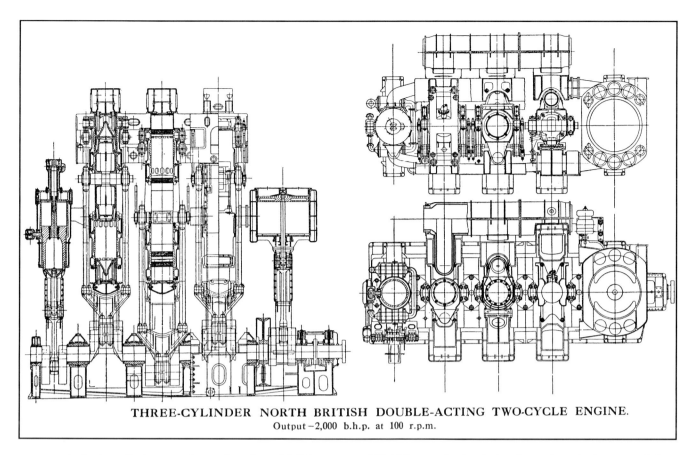

THREE-CYLINDER NORTH BRITISH DOUBLE-ACTING TWO-CYCLE ENGINE.
Output – 2,000 b.h.p. at 100 r.p.m.

A single-cylinder experimental engine of 24" bore was built, also a smaller two-cylinder unit (bore 11.5", stroke 14.5", 240 BHP) which went to sea on board one of the British India ships, *Dumana* (8428/1923) delivered in March 1923. Powering one of the three generator sets, later in the year it was removed, replaced by a North British single-acting, four-stroke unit similar to those already powering the other two generators.

The first production main engine went to yard number 596, launched as *Swanley* on 22nd March 1924. She was a typical 9,200 deadweight tramp of the period, a shelter decker with topgallant forecastle and split superstructure between straight bow and counter stern. Dimensions were 410 feet by 55 feet beam and 29 feet depth to upper deck. The engine was a three-cylinder unit (bore 24.5", stroke 44", 2,000 BHP) which gave 11 knots. There was nothing about her to indicate she was the first British-built ship powered by a double-acting diesel. It had been agreed in January 1923 that she be registered to a new company, the Swanley Shipping Co. Ltd., jointly (50:50) owned by Harris and Dixon Ltd. and companies in the Swan Hunter group (Swan Hunter, Barclay, Curle and North British). Her price was £110,000.

The second Maclagan was allocated in May 1924 to number 608, a joint speculative venture by Barclay, Curle and North British intended for management by Hopemount Shipping Co. Ltd. Hopemount dated from June 1904 when formed as a shipowning subsidiary of Swan Hunter, and remained in their ownership until sold to Common Brothers in 1966. Many shipbuilders had related owning companies for various reasons. As well as simple commercial ventures they might give work for younger scions of the family, operate speculative ships built to keep the yard working and awaiting a buyer, handle old ships taken in part exchange for new, or run vessels with new or experimental features, such as the Maclagan.

Yard number 608, a sister to *Swanley*, was launched on 31st March 1925. With a similar engine she cost £126,000 and a Trade Facility Act (TFA) guarantee for £75,000 was obtained. A sale to Otto Andersen and Co., Oslo, for £123,800 was cancelled when they failed to make the first payment. Placed with Hopemount, she was chartered to Ellerman's Hall Line for three years from delivery in August 1925. Launched as 608 she was named *Frederick Gilbert* whilst fitting out, but entered service as *City of Stockholm*.

The third engine was a larger four-cylinder unit of 2,700 BHP with the same bore and stroke. This was fitted to number 613, a speculative tanker the hull of which duplicated *Nausicaa* (5,005/1922), built by the North of Ireland Shipbuilding Co. Ltd. She was a typical engines-aft tanker of 7,850 deadweight on dimensions of 388 feet by 52 feet by 29 feet depth. Again Hopemount would be fallback owners and TFA guarantees were sought. But a Norwegian buyer was found and she was launched on 12th May 1926 as *Storsten* (5,343/1926) for the Tonsbergs Rederi A/S, Tonsberg, managed by Birger Rafen.

None of the three operators were happy with their vessels, complaining about the many engine breakdowns experienced. In 1926 a committee briefed to examine the problem reported it was 'unwise to make further engines.' Work on another four-cylinder unit stopped, and the following year this and the test engine were scrapped. Future diesel production would be centred on a Doxford licence obtained by Barclay, Curle in 1926.

It was agreed all three ships be re-engined at builders' expense. In 1927 the Maclagan in *Swanley* was replaced by a 3-cylinder Barclay, Curle Doxford 58L3 (580mm bore, 2,320mm stroke, 2,250 BHP). Group holding in the Swanley Shipping Co. Ltd. increased to 75%, and then 100%. Finally, in 1932, *Swanley* was transferred to Hopemount and renamed *Hoperange*. *Storsten* was taken in hand during 1928 and emerged with a similar Barclay, Curle Doxford rated at 2,100 BHP. *City of Stockholm* was re-engined in 1927, converted to a steamer at Swan Hunter's Neptune works. They built her triple-expansion engine which took steam from three boilers at 200psi to give 3,100 IHP and 11.75 knots. On completion she was sold for £85,000 to the Venatus Shipping Co. Ltd, which was 51% Swan Hunter-owned and was managed by Howard Tenens Ltd. In 1932 she joined her sister in the Hopemount fleet as *Hopetor*.

In reviewing the Maclagan, A.C. Hardy in his *History of Motorshipping* concluded it was '...a very gallant and ingenious attempt to couple the manifest advantages of double-acting with a solution to the difficult problem of the lower combustion space, its gland, and the pierced lower cylinder cover.'

Vessels fitted with a Maclagan diesel

1. SWANLEY
ON 147681 4,950g 3,058n 9,170d 411.9 x 55.4 x 26.3 feet. Shelter deck.
3-cyl. 2SCDA Maclagan diesel engine by North British Diesel Engine Works (1922) Ltd., Glasgow; bore 24.5", stroke 44"; 2,000 BHP, 10 knots.
1927: Re-engined with an opposed-piston, 3-cyl. Doxford 58L3 diesel engine by Barclay, Curle and Co. Ltd., Glasgow; bore 580mm, stroke 2,320mm; 2,250 BHP.
22.3.1924: Launched by Barclay, Curle and Co. Ltd., Glasgow (Yard No. 596).
6.1924: Completed for Swanley Shipping Co. Ltd. (Harris and Dixon Ltd., managers), London as SWANLEY.
1932: Sold to Hopemount Shipping Co. Ltd. (A. Stott and Co. Ltd., managers), Newcastle-on-Tyne and renamed HOPERANGE.
1937: Sold to D/S A/S Vard (Jacobsen and Salvesen, managers), Oslo, Norway and renamed HIRD.
15.9.1940: Torpedoed by the German submarine U 65 in position 58.00 north by 12.20 west, straggling from convoy HX72, on a voyage from Panama City, Mobile and Bermuda to Manchester, with 8,101 tons of general cargo and 197 tons black carbon.

2. CITY OF STOCKHOLM
ON 147326 5,017g 3,124n 9,433d 411.8 x 55.4 x 26.3 feet. Shelter deck.
3-cyl. 2SCDA Maclagan diesel engine by North British Diesel Engine Works (1922) Ltd., Glasgow; bore 24.5", stroke 44"; 2,000 BHP, 10.5 knots.
1927: Re-engined with T. 3-cyl. by Swan, Hunter and Wigham Richardson Ltd., Newcastle-on-Tyne; bores 25.5", 42" and 70", stroke 48"; 3,100 IHP; 11.75 knots. 3 boilers, 200 psi.
31.3.1925: Launched by Barclay, Curle and Co. Ltd., Glasgow as Yard No. 608, then named FREDERICK GILBERT .
8.1925: Completed for Hopemount Shipping Co. Ltd., Newcastle on Tyne for a three-year charter to Hall Line Ltd., Liverpool (Ellerman Lines Ltd., London, managers) as CITY OF STOCKHOLM.
1927: Owners became Hopemount Shipping Co. Ltd. (Stamp, Mann and Co., managers), Newcastle-on-Tyne.
1927: Sold to Venatus Shipping Co. Ltd. (Howard Tenens Ltd., managers), London and renamed PRUNUS.
1932: Owners became Hopemount Shipping Co. Ltd. (A. Stott and Co. Ltd., managers), Newcastle-on-Tyne and renamed HOPETOR.
1937: Sold to Barry Shipping Co. Ltd. (B. and S. Steam Shipping Co. Ltd.), Cardiff and renamed ST MERRIEL.
1939: Owners restyled South American Saint Line Ltd.
2.1.1943: Bombed and sunk by German aircraft at Bone.
1950: Raised.
4.8.1950: Foundered off Cape Noli, in tow for breakers at Savona.

3. STORSTEN
5343g 3114n 7850d 388.1 x 52.7 x 29.0 feet. Tanker.
4-cyl. 2SCDA Maclagan diesel engine by North British Diesel Engine Works (1922) Ltd., Glasgow; bore 24.5", stroke 44" 2,700 BHP.
1928: Re-engined with an opposed-piston, 3-cyl. Doxford 58L3 diesel engine by Barclay, Curle and Co. Ltd., Glasgow; bore 580mm, stroke 2,320mm; 2,100 BHP; 11 knots.
12.5.1926: Launched by Barclay, Curle and Co. Ltd., Glasgow (Yard No. 613).
1926: Completed for Tonsberg Rederi A/S (Birger Rafen, manager), Tonsberg, Norway as STORSTEN.
1.4.1941: Struck a floating mine and sank 32 miles south of Christiansand whilst on a voyage from Gothenburg for the UK.

Seen here docking at Avonmouth, *Hoperange* ex-*Swanley* was probably a standard hull: compare her appearance with *City of Stockholm/Hopetor* opposite.

City of Stockholm (top) was renamed *Prunus* in 1927 and *Hopetor* (middle) in 1932, her last change of name came in 1937 when sold to the South American Saint Line as *St Merriel.* As such she was bombed when the Luftwaffe attacked Bone Harbour on 2nd January 1943. Hit in the engine room and bridge, she was a total loss. The wreck was raised in 1950 and left in tow for the breakers at Savona, only to founder on 4th August 1950 off Cape Noli. *[Top: Ian Farquhar collection; middle: Ivor Rooke collection]*

Rejuvenated by her Doxford engine *Storsten* (bottom, at Preston) remained in the Norwegian tanker fleet until sunk on 1st April 1941. Norwegian ships were trapped in Swedish ports when German troops occupied Norway. In January 1941 five broke out to reach Britain in Operation Rubble, led by George Binney. In March 1942 Binney organised Operation Performance, a second attempt with ten ships. Two reached Britain, two turned back and the others were sunk by alerted German forces or scuttled when stopped. *Storsten* foundered after striking a floating mine.

SOOT, SEAWATER, AND CYLINDER OIL
Some family memories by Ian Muir

After serving his apprenticeship with the Fairfield Shipbuilding and Engineering Works in Govan, my grandfather John Kerr Muir went to sea as an engineer, like so many of his time. Of his various adventures, that surrounded by the strangest circumstances was surely what he experienced while serving as Third Engineer on the cargo steamer *Ventnor* (3,961/1901) of Gow, Harrison and Co., Glasgow. Launched by Russell and Co., Port Glasgow on 23rd January 1901, she had triple-expansion engines by Rankin and Blackmore of Eagle Foundry, Greenock, developing 2,000 horse power and taking steam from two Scotch boilers working at 180 pounds on the square inch.

A one-way trip
One of several ships chartered by the Admiralty for the purpose, *Ventnor* carried coal to the China naval station for bunkering the fleet. To give an insight into such tramp ship operation in those times it may be noted that her first voyage lasted 432 days - and was by no means unusual at that. Her second voyage took her to New Zealand and lasted 179 days, but proved to be a virtual one-way trip.

Ventnor arrived at Chelsea Wharf, Auckland, from Java on 22nd October 1902 and, besides 5,357 tons of Westport coal, loaded for return to China for reburial coffins containing the remains of 499 Chinese who had died in the Dominion; some having done so as long as 20 years previously. This strange parcel of cargo aroused some interest in the city at the time, and there may have been some old salts who looked on such an odyssey with foreboding, but the weather was clear and the sea calm when she left Wellington at 09.30 am on 26th October bound for Hong Kong. By early afternoon she had put the Cook Straight between the North and South Islands behind her and set a course which would clear Cape Egmont on the west coast of North Island with an offing of five to six miles on the starboard hand. Mount Egmont stands at 8,260 feet so must have been readily visible in daylight in clear weather, but at 12.40 am on 27th the ship struck a reef believed later to be south of Cape Egmont. By going astern she was able to free herself but had been holed, and the water gained steadily against the pumps. By the morning of the 28th her bow was low in the water and by that evening beneath it, making her unmanageable. At 21.00 the order was given to abandon ship and the British officers and Chinese crewmen had scarcely cleared away in the four lifeboats when she plunged bow-first to the bottom.

They were reckoned then to be about 10 miles from the light on Hokianga Head, and all boats set course in that direction. At daybreak two of them with a total of 14 survivors made a landing at Omapere Beach; the mate, second engineer, and my grandfather being among them. Later that day the wooden steamer *Energy* (58/1899) arrived at Hokianga Heads having picked up the third boat's crew comprising six Europeans and four Chinese. The boat was full of water when encountered, and the crew exhausted. A search was then organised for the fourth boat containing Captain Henry George Ferry, other officers and remaining crew members, but no trace was found until 11th November, when wreckage was washed ashore at Hukatere. The surviving records of Gow, Harrison and Co. quote eight lives lost, being master, chief engineer, two junior officers, and four crew.

One account states that nine of the crew were aged Chinese body attendants, carried to take care of their deceased compatriots, though by what means they were to do so was not explained. How many of these joined their charges in a watery grave does not seem to have been recorded, but the 24 survivors left Omapere on 5th November for Auckland. Their story was recounted in the *Auckland Weekly News* of 13th November and one of the photographs accompanying the report shows the surviving officers posing awkwardly in new suits, everyone having lost their possessions. Gow, Harrison and Co. managed to weather the loss, receiving £54,949 from their underwriters; going on to own further tramp steamers whose names began with the letter V, but which did not include a further *Ventnor*.

Coasting and sweeping
Grandfather is recalled stating that it was after returning home from this narrow escape that he decided to take a break to study and sit for his ticket. He must have chosen that time to marry too and then, not surprisingly, opted to work on coastal vessels which would bring him home to Glasgow from time to time. For the Clyde Shipping Co. he sailed on *Aranmore*, but with David MacBrayne is known to have served on several vessels. Most notable of these was the venerable *Glencoe* which dated from as far back as 1846 and paddled almost every route her owners operated, but is perhaps best associated with the Kyle to Portree passage when commanded by Captain Baxter. She was built and engined by David Tod and John McGregor, both trained by David Napier the famous pioneer of steamboat design and operation on the Clyde and Thames. Her single-cylinder engine was of the steeple type he had conceived late one night and had drawn down there and then upon the dining room floor! Grandfather delighted to tell how the greaser had to go up to the weather deck and open the doors of a little wooden house to oil her single crosshead as it bobbed up and down within.

He was still on the west coast of Scotland when the First World War broke out but in 1915 was directed to take over as chief engineer of the requisitioned Glasgow and South Western Railway paddler *Juno*, lying at Greenock. Britain had found itself unprepared for war in many ways, not least regarding specialised vessels for keeping vital coastal shipping lanes clear of mines. The number of losses mounted, and matters were near crisis point before the Admiralty bowed to the suggestion made by a Lieutenant Saunders RN that the many shallow-draft paddle steamers which operated ferry and pleasure services in the estuaries around Britain in peacetime might be

Glencoe began her long life as Mary Jane, named after the wife of James Matheson of Stornoway, who plied her on his Glasgow route giving calls at island and mainland piers in both directions. Built of iron in 1846 by David Tod and John McGregor she had an old-world appearance, with fiddle bow, bowsprit, figurehead, gaff sails on two masts, and main deck devoid of any saloons to afford shelter from the inhospitable Minch. She was propelled by a steeple engine having a single cylinder of 56 x 54 inches, rated at 177 NHP. She was sold to the Glasgow and Lochfyne Steam Packet Co. in 1851, then to David Hutcheson in 1857. Daniel Brown's splendidly atmospheric photograph shows her calling at Tarbert, Loch Fyne, probably in 1856 (upper). The precarious-looking plank gangway would give crew access to the bow for anchoring and mooring when livestock were penned on the foredeck. She was destined for greater things however, Hutcheson having noted her qualities. In 1875 she was taken in hand,

lengthened from 149.5 to 165.4 feet, and modernised in appearance and appointments by fitting a straight slanting stem, six-vent paddleboxes, removal of foremast gaff and mainmast complete, and provision of a saloon on the after deck (lower). In her new guise as Glencoe she was to become famous. [Mrs. Georgina Steward.]

converted easily and effectively for minesweeping. Saunders was given P. and A. Campbells' Bristol Channel paddle steamers Devonia and Bristol Queen, plus a short period in which to prove his theory, which he quickly did. Accordingly, ships of this type were soon being converted for duty all round the coast, Juno being the first Clyde steamer to hoist the White Ensign. In those days, before the invention of the paravane, a device allowing a single ship to sweep effectively while keeping out of danger if favoured with luck, it was the practice to stream sweep wires between two ships of similar size and performance. These cut the moorings of submerged mines which then bobbed to the surface and were destroyed by gunfire or, in a few hair-raising cases, retrieved complete for inspection.

According to grandfather, the Admiralty had to send Campbells' Britannia back round to the Clyde to provide a suitable partner for Juno, and I can recall clearly grandfather telling me further as a young boy how '...we were sent out to run trials on the measured mile against her.... I had the racing valves (his term), everything open, and we beat the Britannia. They told us later we had done 22 knots.' Years later when I had learned more about steamers and the nature of such a contest I asked him about the subject again, and the second version of the story tallied with what I remembered from the earlier telling. Juno's mean speed on trial in 1898 had been 19.26 knots, while that of her slightly smaller and nominally less powerful consort had been about half a knot more. Campbells'

Beginning with the flagship *Glen Sannox* in 1892, J. and G. Thomson Ltd. of Clydebank had built four paddle steamers for the Glasgow and South Western Railway Company in the 1890s, all highly successful in their differing duties. Thus it seems no surprise that when their successors, the Clydebank Engineering and Shipbuilding Co. Ltd., found themselves with a partially-built paddle steamer on their hands as a result of their client's withdrawal, it was the Sou' West who were approached in hope of interest. They jumped at the chance and with a few modifications *Juno* was added to the fleet in 1898, taking station at Ayr for the cruise traffic. Believed to have been ordered to operate excursions from the south of England, she was built to heavier scantlings than the usual Clyde steamer, but was thus well-suited for the boisterous conditions which can be experienced in the lower Firth. She was 245 x 29.1 x 9.7 feet, and achieved a mean of 19.26 knots on the Skelmorlie mile, being propelled by an impressive compound diagonal engine of 325 NHP with cylinders of 33 and 7l by

60 inch stroke taking steam from an eight-furnace double-ended boiler working under forced draught. She was a splendid ship in those heady days, but a big girl with a hearty appetite which resulted in her otherwise untimely withdrawal by the LMS in 1932. She was broken up at Alloa, mourned by many.

The upper photograph shows *Juno* in G&SWR colours entering Ayr, and in the lower she is heading upstream past Gourock in London, Midland and Scottish Railway colours with black hull and yellow funnel. *[Both: author's collection]*

steamers were always run at the limit of their performance, however, and none more than this, their flagship, which held all Bristol Channel pier-to-pier records worth noting down, and was frequently timed at 20 knots over considerable distances throughout her long life. Besides seeing off all her fleetmates she also waved her ensign under the bows of everything that rival shipowners, including railway companies, could set against her. Undeniably, she was one of the most successful paddle steamers every put in the water. How *Juno* managed to best her on that occasion remains a mystery - and a very contentious one. Bristol Channel steamer enthusiasts were and remain devotees of the stop-watch, and to suggest even

now that anything short of a destroyer with feathering safety valves ever got to windward of their favourite is to preach heresy of quite the darkest shade. George Owen of Swansea kindly furnished information he transcribed in 1957 from Campbells' Memorandum Book of 1915 (which may no longer exist) and this shows that *Britannia* and *Glen Usk* both left Bristol on 5th February 1915 for Harland and Wolffs' yard, Glasgow, the intention being that they would make a sweeping pair. They duly set out together as planned, and it is believed that, in fact, it was only after HMS *Glen Usk* proved an ill-matched consort that *Juno* was brought in to pair HMS *Britain*, as *Britannia* had now become. It could well have been at that point that some joust took place, but there is no record of any such encounter in the otherwise detailed record referred to. Yet I have never doubted the basic truth of grandfather's story, though explaining, let alone substantiating it, is another matter. Certainly it would be to *Juno's* great credit if she won since none of her own crew familiar with her ways went to war with her. Grandfather imparted no knowledge of the comparative states of both ships, whether one or both were stripped of peacetime fittings, whether one or both were laden down with the weight of newly-installed sweeping gear, whether one had good coal, the other bad. There should have been little amiss with *Britain's* steaming ability since Dunsmuir and Jackson of Govan had provided her with a new boiler in 1912. When refitted after the war she proved capable of over 20 knots in Bideford Bay, her engines turning 53 rpm against the 49.5 on her original trials - not much deference to advancing years. What a boat! *Juno*, by comparison, had spent most of her life on summer cruises from Ayr Harbour, her berth only yards from *Britannia's* birthplace in the yard of S. McKnight and Co. This trade kept her apart from much of the daily cut and thrust for the Clyde's hotly-contested commuter traffic, so there is likely no equivalent record detailing her exploits. She was no slouch though, as she sometimes proved, but it has to be said the chances of her achieving 22 knots in any trim seem likely to have been remote.

The 12th Minesweeping Flotilla

The true story may never be known, but no matter the outcome the crews worked in harmony as a team. Grandfather became friendly with his opposite number, Campbells' well-known, bearded, chief engineer Alphonso Scott. Their ships swept in the same flotilla out to Rathlin Island and on to the Hebrides, then in the Cromarty Firth for a spell before moving south to the Firth of Forth where they were based at Granton's Middle Pier to maintain the swept channel out past the Isle of May. Seeking to find out what I could about the mystery I wrote to *Sea Breezes* and received a touching letter, whose relevant part is worth reproducing in full.

Royal Alfred Seamens Home, Belvedere, Kent.
Dear Mr Muir,
I was very interested in your letter in this months *Sea Breezes* re PS *Junior* (ex-*Juno*). I knew her well, and your grandfather, also all the Officers. I joined the PS *Britain* (ex-*Britannia*) as a Sub Lieutenant RNR in 1915 after coming out of the old Allan Line of Glasgow where I was serving as 4th Officer in the RMS *Grampian*. The 12th Minesweeping Flotilla stationed at Granton consisted of 6 paddle sweepers keeping the Firth of Forth clear of mines. *St Elvies* (flagship), *Paris* (ex S W Ry.), *Britain* (ex-*Britannia*), *Junior* (ex-*Juno*), *Kylemore* - I forget the sixth one. As we did not sweep in the dark we used to have some jolly evenings at the Granton Hotel, or the Commercial at Leith. *Juno* was our chum ship, and I remember your grandfather coming on board to see our chief Mr Scott many times. I would not like to say which was the fastest ship, though all were perhaps except *Kylemore* and *Paris*. But P. and A. Campbells' three sister ships *Britannia*, *Cambria*, and *Westward Ho* could move. I remember one night expecting an air raid when *Britannia* was sent from Leith Roads as anti-aircraft protection, the distance as the crow flies being 20 miles. *Britannia* did it in one hour five minutes via the boom gateway, which put another few miles on our distance. *Britannia* and *Juno* could do 12 knots with the sweep wires down. I was about a year in *Britannia*.
Yours sincerely,
W. Glass.

The crew of HMS *Britain* in a shot believed taken in 1915 or 1916. The master, seated centre, is Campbell's popular Captain Adam Livingstone and, in view of the date, one of the other officers could be Mr. Glass. Sadly, the picture did not come into the writer's possession until long after our contact. Identifications appreciated. *[Author's collection]*

Grampian of 1907, and her sister *Hesperian* of 1908 were both built by Stephen of Linthouse, Glasgow, the last ships planned, built, and commissioned by the Allan Line of Glasgow. Being for their owners' intermediate service, both were twin-screw steamers propelled by triple-expansion engines. *Grampian* was 485.3 x 60.2 x 38.1 feet, and of 10,947 tons gross. She was to come to an ignominious end. Having passed, with other Allan Line assets, to Canadian Pacific Steamships Ltd. in 1917, she was undergoing a post-war refit at Antwerp when damaged by fire on 14th March 1921. Abandoned to underwriters, she lay around until July 1925 when sold to Frank Rijsdijk and broken up at Hendrik ido Ambacht. [*Wotherspoon Collection, Mitchell Library, Glasgow*]

The flagship of the 12th Minesweeping Flotilla was *St. Elvies*, Fairfield-built in 1896 for the Liverpool and North Wales Steamship Co. Ltd. Seen here in the Menai Straits during the 1920s, *St. Elvies* was withdrawn in 1930 and broken up at Birkenhead.

Other correspondence followed from the late Alex Taylor of Stoke Bishop, Bristol, a lifelong Campbell hand. He joined HMS *Britain* in March 1918 but could throw no light upon the matter except to list her many record pier-to-pier times, those not set by Captain Peter Campbell himself being held by Alex's father, Captain Daniel Taylor, who started with Captain Bob (father of Peter and Alex Campbell) around 1881. It was Daniel Taylor who stuck his head through the open rear window of *Britannia's* engine room one day to ask newly appointed Chief Fred Halse, ex-*Cambria*, 'Hows she going Fred?' 'Going?' he replied, 'I cant stop the bugger!'

Sub Lieutenant Glass must have joined HMS *Britain* shortly after the fabled duel of speed, and since both he and grandfather served only around a year on their respective ships neither would have met up with Alex Taylor. He died some years ago aged around 90 so there must be few others who know anything of such matters now. Perhaps though, in some dusty Admiralty archive....

At Fairfields

Grandfather was twice on cargo ships torpedoed in the war, though how those events fit into the chronology is not known. Apart from the loss of a middle fingertip while making one of these escapes he came through unscathed. In 1917 he was back in Fairfields working on the building of the ill-fated steam turbine submarine *K 13*, and one of many who were bitterly disappointed to read an amended list of builder's personnel who were to have a place on board during her trials; his name having been included on an earlier provisional list. Disappointment was short lived and any relief put out of mind in the round-the-clock rescue operation mounted when she failed to surface from a dive off Shandon in the Gareloch. Some worked without rest for sixty hours in the making and fitting of rescue apparatus. Thirty-one men lost their lives in the tragedy, the tablet in Elder Park across the road from the yard bearing mute witness alike to selfless heroism of the rescuers and the folly of the blinkered brasshats who pressed ahead with such a project. Fairfields refitted the salvaged wreck and completed her sister *K 14*, but never built another submarine.

The Mariners Home

My grandmother, Mary Muir, died in 1948 after a short illness, and father and mother speculated as to what was likely to be the best course, since mother's mother already lived with us and we did not have room to accommodate another relative. Before long their problem was solved by grandfather's own announcement that he intended selling up and going to live at Sir Gabriel Woods Mariners Home in Newark Street, Greenock. And that he duly did.

This excellent institution was opened in 1850 as an asylum for aged master mariners and merchant seamen, Gabriel Wood being a son of the town who had prospered as a servant of the British Government, mostly in the West Indies. On his death in 1845 he left funds and the wish that his widow and sister should see through his intention to inaugurate something of the kind. They did, and the splendid building survives still, continuing to do its work under the direction of the British Sailors Society who took over from the Trustees some years ago. The latter were

still at the helm during grandfather's time as an inmate, and not for them the delegation of daily management to some social worker or overweening do-gooder. They retained to the last a very clear view of the sort of person they saw best able to run such an establishment in ship-shape fashion, and that was a master mariner. By the time the writer became a frequent visitor the supply of suitable salts in possession of a square-rig ticket must have dried up, but there was a definite awareness about the place that such would be preferable, were it obtainable. Not that standards had been allowed to slip. The threshold was painted an unsullied white that would have graced an Admiral's quarterdeck, while the door's brass kickplate had a polish fit to make archangels sing and St Peter cast about for something of the same gauge to grace whatever gangway he keeps greased for seafarers. The flawless gleam on the hall linoleum was only slightly less obvious owing to the lower light level within, filtered by the window presiding over the staircase. The Captain's Office lay to starboard upon going aboard, a statement composed with care since it had been learned by experience that were one inept enough to enquire from this eminence whether grandfather was in, a salvo carefully couched in the approved terminology would strike to the vitals informing that, no, Chief Muir went ashore at Four Bells with Captain Robb - you'll likely find them in their usual seat on the Esplanade. And, often enough, there they were. It was not that they were hard to spot since in those days inmates of officer rank wore a blue uniform with peaked cap, their reefer jacket having two rows of brass buttons. Other ranks wore the same, but with a single row of buttons. As such they were well known to dwellers 'neath the Green Oak and pointed out to youngsters as old sailors worthy of respect - but sometimes visitors were not so well-informed. On summer Saturdays it was my ploy to get out on Gourock Pier for a close look at the paddle and turbine steamers constantly arriving and departing in those days, but Grandfather was reluctant to be drawn there, for the uniform had its disadvantages in his experience. 'If I go there in this rig-out a lot of drunks and wifies wi' weans 'll think I'm on the railway and want to know the times o' a' the steamers', he protested. Thus it was that our chat and walk were usually on or along the Esplanade - which was all right if the youthful could last the pace. On one occasion a chill easterly had swirled all others from the seats yet the two old seadogs were coatless, the wind soughing in the front of grandfathers jacket and out at his cuffs while I bent against the blast with collar up. Father once reported a similar experience. The Captain at least had the sense to subject only his starboard quarter to the weather, but then he was a former ships' master from the north east of Scotland who did have a square-rig ticket in his pocket and must have sought many fair winds from that direction. At eighty years old his five feet were still straight, immaculate, and raked back like a mast, his eyes a bright piercing blue beneath a full head of white hair. By the cut of his canvas he must have been a martinet in his day, but had mellowed to a charming old gentleman and pleasant companion. Grandfather finally rounded up and came to his last anchorage in 1959 aged 85, having had scarcely a day's illness in his life. On one of my last visits he expressed surprise and pleasure that he had lived long enough to see his only grandson follow in his footsteps as an engineer at sea. Of the few well dones received in a varied life that is perhaps the most prized.

The remarkable life and times of *Britannia* are depicted in this spread of photographs, spanning sixty years and two wars.

P. and A. Campbell Ltd. awarded her contract to Hutson and Son, Marine Engineers, of Kelvinhaugh, Glasgow. They subcontracted the hull to S. McKnight and Co. Ltd., of Ayr, who launched her on 14th May 1896. She was propelled by a Hutson compound diagonal having cylinders of 37 & 67 by 66 inch stroke, rated at 304 BHP, and she is believed to have made over 19 knots on trial, a figure later improved upon after fitting new paddle wheels. The first photograph was taken before her trials, and shows a particularly prominent stay for her funnel. It seems that this was soon removed, however, as it is absent in trials shots, and in the second photograph taken as she entered Ilfracombe, believed to be on her first day in service, 29th June 1896. As Campbell's flagship, her career got off to a spectacular start, with extended cruises beyond the Bristol Channel to Penzance, Falmouth and the Scilly Isles, and to Plymouth and the Channel Isles. She also made visits to the Solent for naval reviews in 1897 and 1902.

First World War service as HMS *Britain* - there was already a pre-Dreadnought battleship named HMS *Britannia* - is covered in the accompanying article (third photograph,

showing her single six-pounder gun). Following her decommissioning in April 1919, she returned to the Bristol Channel, where P. and A. Campbell now had the excursion business almost to themselves, and judging from the fourth photograph opposite *Britannia* was restored to her former glory.

The Second World War saw her called up once again, but this time named HMS *Skiddaw* taking the pennant number J 80 (top photograph this page). The second shows her triumphant, if rather war-weary, return to Bristol on 18th May 1945 - her bridge structure appears to have been heightened somewhat during the conflict.

Britannia made her first post-war cruise on 1st June 1946, but disgraced herself and had to be withdrawn in July when her boiler failed. She was not returned to service until 1948, fitted with a double-ended boiler which necessitated the second funnel. The bottom photograph, taken in June 1949, probably when she was running on the south coast, shows her in remarkable condition for a ship in her fifty-third year.

In 1956 P. and A. Campbell decided to retire the *Britannia* and on 19th September she ran a special farewell trip from Bristol to Ilfracombe. However, failures in other members of the fleet meant she spent a further week on the Cardiff to Weston service. She almost had a further reprieve, and was actually sold to Belgians who intended to use her temporarily as an accommodation ship before breaking her up, but an export license was refused. On 7th December the 60-year old ship was towed from Penarth to Newport, to be broken up by John Cashmore Ltd. *[Ilfracombe photograph: Nigel Coombes collection; HMS Britain: Peter Newall; all others: Ballast Trust]*

BRITISH MERCHANT SHIPS IN THE MEXICAN REVOLUTION

David H. Grover

The backwaters of war often witness events as interesting as those that occur in important and well-documented battles. Ships flying the red ensign are sometimes completely on their own in navigating these backwaters, a situation that calls for a high order of resourcefulness from their captains. This is the story of a small group of British freighters on the Pacific coast of Mexico at the time of the First World War, and the adventures they created for themselves.

When the First World War began, the shooting phase of the Mexican revolution had been going on for about two years. These two major conflicts, overlapping as they did, produced some strange maritime happenings in the coastal waters of Mexico. This was particularly true along the west coast of that country where, absent both north-south rail service and an adequate Mexican merchant fleet, ships of a number of nationalities had provided the only link to the outside world for several good-size urban areas and a number of smaller port cities.

The diversity of the nations that provided merchant shipping and naval patrols along this coast reflected the number and nationality of the foreigners who lived in enclaves of agriculture and mining in northwest Mexico. For decades two of Mexico's most famous Presidents, Benito Juarez and Porfirio Diaz, had made generous land grants to foreign individuals and companies to encourage the development of the area. Upon the outbreak of hostilities in the revolution tens of thousands of foreigners resided in the states of Baja California, Sonora, and Sinaloa.

The United States, of course, had the largest fleet of merchant and naval vessels on Mexico's west coast, but British and German merchant ships also served the area, while naval vessels of those two nations as well as France and Japan watched over their respective expatriate colonies ashore. US, German, and British consuls served these expatriates, but in the wildest moments of the revolution these officials had to be evacuated to safety along with their constituents. The challenge to foreign-flag merchant ships was to be ready at any time to evacuate foreigners of any nationality to safety, and to avoid being seized by over-zealous Mexican officials while still turning a profit for their owners.

Fortunately, early in the revolution the captains of the ships of these countries, both merchant and naval, developed a genuine camaraderie in working together in evacuating groups of foreigners during the frequent periods of violence which were directed toward non-Mexicans. During these evacuations the Canadian and British ships flying the red ensign set an example of providing refuge to foreigners in a way that combined compassion, gallantry, good business acumen, and a bit of luck. One ship in particular stood out, serving as the unofficial flagship of the merchant fleet on Mexico's west coast: the steamer *Cetriana*.

WEST COAST OF MEXICO

INSET: EXTREME SOUTH   (Same scale)

Activities of the *Cetriana*

This freighter, built as the *Norway* by Grangemouth Dockyard Company in 1891, was only 203 feet long and measured 939 gross tons. She had been a regular on the Mexican coast for several years, as well as being known at ports in California and British Columbia. Owned by W. Eadie in Vancouver but registered in Glasgow, she was commanded by Captain Edward J. Minister, who was a Lieutenant in the RNR, that reserve component of the Royal Navy made up of officers of the merchant service.

In April 1914 this ship had stopped at several ports along the middle section of the Mexican coast to pick up Americans and civilians of other nationalities who were anxious to leave for their own safety. On 25th April she was at Mazatlan where she helped to tow the disabled Federalist gunboat *Moreles* to an anchorage, perhaps an act of assistance to court favour with the local authorities. Since governments changed frequently in Mexico in those days, it was useful if a ship's captain could stay on friendly terms with those ashore who were in authority for the moment, as well as those on the other side who might soon be in control.

Captain Edward J. Minister of the *Cetriana* was responsible for the safety of more than 150 people who were fleeing from the perils of the Mexican revolution. *[Sunset Magazine]*

The *Cetriana*, shown here at Manzanillo with the cruiser *Maryland* in the distance, was the centre of several dangerous incidents that might have led to serious international consequences. *[Puget Sound Maritime Historical Society]*

On 26th April the little British steamer called briefly at the small port of San Blas, about 120 miles farther down the coast. Here she picked up about a dozen thoroughly terrified refugees who had fled from hostile mobs. Their leader, an American mining man, had been imprisoned by the local Federalist general for surrendering dynamite to the rebels. Captain Minister went ashore to arbitrate the matter with the authorities, and succeeded in obtaining the prisoner's release when the man was able to show that the explosives had been taken from him at the threat of his life.

The next day when the *Cetriana* arrived at Manzanillo Captain Minister found that the German steamship *Marie* (1,866/1905) had recently been anchored there with a load of refugees. One of the passengers was a US businessman from the small inland city of Colima. He had been taken off the *Marie* and held captive by the local commander, General Verregua, who ordered that he be shot as a spy, under the pretext that the man was a personal friend of President Woodrow Wilson to whom he had allegedly communicated information about the situation in Mexico.

This man was eventually saved by the intervention of a local resident, Fritz G. Keyser, who identified himself to Verregua's officials as the German consul. Noting that the American had been accorded the protection of the German flag, Keyser obtained the release of the man, and directed the bewildered captain of the German ship to leave port. In reality, Keyser was not the consul; he had merely assumed the role for two weeks during which he successfully carried off several episodes in which Americans and Europeans were extricated from dangerous situations.

Further trouble developed when the *Cetriana* was ready to leave Manzanillo the following day with 113 US refugees on board. Possibly smarting at being forced to yield his prisoner to the ersatz German consul who had now boarded the *Cetriana*, General Verregua decided to have the ship's pier mined with dynamite and soaked with oil, preparatory to burning it. This action was a part of his personal declaration of war against the United States.

The General also arranged to block the escape of the ship, with the Mexican steam schooner *Luella*

(412/1898) occupying all the manoeuvering room of the British ship at the pier and putting her mooring lines over the top of those of the *Cetriana*. In addition, the Mexican troopships *Manuel Herrerias* and *General Pesqueria* stood by to block her escape route. When Captain Minister protested to the port authorities, he was told that he had thirty minutes to get underway before the pier was torched.

This boatload of refugees coming out to the *Cetriana* at Manzanillo was under the personal protection of the German consul at that port, an official whose fraudulence was exceeded only by his bravery. *[Sunset Magazine]*

The top photograph of the pier at Manzanillo, taken from the deck of the *Cetriana*, shows the steam schooner *Luella* on the right, and the two Mexican transports on the left. *[Sunset Magazine]*

Another view taken from the *Cetriana* (middle) shows the billowing cloud of smoke created when the local military authorities at Manzanillo torched a pier as an act of defiance against the United States. *[Sunset Magazine]*

The subject of the painting to the right, the USS *Raleigh*, was one of the older cruisers of the US Navy which saw duty in Mexican waters during the revolution in that country. She helped the British steamer *Cetriana* get out of Manzanillo with refugees from the terror of the Mexican revolution. *[US Navy]*

As the captain worked the *Cetriana* out of her tight confinement, the decks of the ship were peppered with rifle fire from the nearby transports which were also getting underway. One of these ships, the *Manuel Herrerias*, even tried to ram her. Shortly thereafter the British steamer was able to clear the dock with her refugees. Within a few minutes the pier was set on fire, and was soon blazing fiercely, along with the *Luella*.

Intervention by the US Navy

Some of these events were observed at a distance when at the same time - late afternoon of 28th April 1914 - the cruiser USS *Raleigh* was preparing to enter the port of Manzanillo when a loud explosion was heard from the inner harbour. Five minutes later additional explosions were heard, and as the cruiser's log noted;

> ...the railroad pier burst into flames. Steamers laying at piers cleared as best they could, one small coasting steamer being caught, and dock and steamer continued burning throughout watch. Several explosions occurred in railroad yards. At 4:45 the British steamer *Cetriana* anchored and the captain came on board with the captain of the American barkentine *Geneva*, the American consul from Acapulco, German consul from Manzanillo.

The *Raleigh*, it seems, had stumbled on to what was becoming one of the most violent reactions against the Americans in Mexico which would be generated along the west coast. One journalist who covered this episode reported that it was the arrival of the US cruiser that actually triggered the decision of the local Federalist commander to implement the violent action ashore. It is more likely, however, that the incendiary activities ashore were already underway when the warship arrived.

As reported by the cruiser's log, on her way out toward the US warship the *Cetriana* had encountered a US sailing ship at anchor in the harbour, the 150-foot two-masted *Geneva* (495/1892). Captain Minister stopped his ship, communicated with W. H. Ferguson, the master of the sailing ship, and subsequently picked up the captain and several refugees who were aboard, as bullets from the two transports continued to fly around the evacuation vessels. While this transfer was underway, two of the refugees on board the sailing vessel returned the Mexican fire with their rifles.

The *Geneva's* captain told an interesting story. His vessel, a brigantine contrary to her designation in the *Raleigh's* logbook, was owned by the South Seas Navigation Company. She had recently discharged a load of hay at San Blas, where authorities told the captain that war between Mexico and the United States had been declared. The captain was not allowed to take on the water and provisions which he needed, but was able to embark a small group of refugees, including a baby, before sailing. Since he did not have enough provisions to head for the nearest US port, Captain Ferguson had taken his ship toward Manzanillo in the hope of encountering an American ship from which he could get the food and water he needed. En route, he was stopped by the Federalist transport *Korrigan II* (289/1892) which had been commandeered from a French-owned copper company in Baja California. This ship escorted the *Geneva* into Manzanillo as a prize of war, a rather questionable action by any interpretation of international law. For several days the captain and his passengers had been detained there as prisoners aboard the *Geneva*.

Captain Ferguson had attempted to contact the *Cetriana* by flag hoist, but the authorities ashore had forbidden the British ship from answering her signals because the *Geneva* was a prize of war. One of the refugees had been allowed to go ashore, however, and this man had been able to contact Captain Minister and make preliminary arrangements for the transfer of the refugees which subsequently took place.

Escape of the *Cetriana*

When the *Cetriana* reached the safety of the USS *Raleigh* farther out in the bay, one of the evacuees, the US consul at Acapulco, related another interesting story to the captain of the cruiser, and later to other US naval authorities. Consul Clement S. Edwards had been able to evacuate his post at Acapulco only by taking passage on a quasi-military Mexican ship, the *General Pesqueria*. Upon arrival at Manzanillo he had not been allowed to land, and was kept a prisoner aboard the transport. The consul was convinced that a particular soldier had been assigned the task of assassinating him if he appeared on deck.

As a condition of his release he was ultimately required to offer safe conduct to Mexican ships. This curious demand may have reflected the fact that Vittoriano Huerta, a man detested by President Woodrow Wilson, was still head of the Mexican Government, and the military officials may have assumed that Wilson's open animosity translated into US ships siding with the revolutionaries. In any case, Consul Edwards readily agreed to the demand which he regarded as meaningless since Mexican ships already had the right of peaceful transit along their own coast in the eyes of the US Navy. After offering this assurance, Edwards was finally allowed to board the *Cetriana*.

With the arrival of the USS *Raleigh* at Manzanillo, and a day or so later the newer and larger cruiser USS *Maryland*, the high-handed officials ashore became more cooperative. Through an aide who visited the captain of the USS *Maryland*, General Verregua quickly toned down his rhetoric, insisting that the entire episode at the pier had been staged by fanatics, for which he was most sorry. However, in opening the champagne on the return courtesy call by representatives from the US naval vessels, the General expressed his regrets that war, nonetheless, would be declared within three days.

At an earlier time, the events at Manzanillo would have been considered an outrage, and might easily have triggered a retaliatory shore bombardment by US naval vessels or a landing by US forces. In fact, the *Raleigh's* log shows that her guns were made ready for instant action, with several five-inch shells placed at each of her main battery weapons and 16 rounds of three-pound ammunition at each of her secondary battery three-pounders. This stepped-up readiness was carried out during the first night when the flames of the burning pier and the *Luella* lit up the sky, and for several subsequent nights when things were quieter in the harbour.

However, under the guidance of the conciliatory trio of leaders of the United States, President Woodrow Wilson, Secretary of State William Jennings Bryan, and Secretary of the Navy Josephus Daniels, the American naval commanders were forced to remain passive, and no action was taken against the Mexican authorities.

Ultimately, the *Cetriana* was able to depart Manzanillo without further trouble. After a few other stops farther to the north, she sailed for San Francisco, reaching the safety of that port on 17th May 1914, with a total of 150 refugees on board. A number of these people told stories of horror, deprivation, captivity, and the death of their travelling companions which had occurred during their attempts to reach the Mexican coast. Certainly these evacuees owed their safety to the determination of the captain of the British ship, the bravado of the pseudo German consul, and the arrival of the American warships.

Always a bit of a risk-taker, the Canadian-owned *Prince Albert* survived two serious strandings in British Columbia early in the First World War but managed to get involved in both evacuations and gun running in the Mexican revolution between her groundings. The photograph to the right shows one of her mishaps. *[Above: Ballast Trust; right: San Francisco Maritime National Historical Park]*

Other ships, other evacuations

Evacuations continued. Not all of the refugees were foreigners; some were Mexicans escaping from the repression of the revolution. Among the score of ships making evacuation runs from Mexico to the United States was another British-flag Canadian steamer which was identified in San Francisco newspapers as the *Prince Albert* which brought a priest and his parishioners to safety in June.

This vessel emerges out of obscurity only to become a mystery ship. *The Guide*, the authoritative shipping publication in San Francisco, shows only one *Prince Albert* on the west coast of North America, a 232-foot long steamer of 1,015 gross tons, built by Earle's in Hull in 1892 for Wilson Line's Hull to Antwerp service as *Bruno*. This ship had been owned since 1910 by the Grand Trunk Railway and registered in Prince Rupert, British Columbia. However, *The Guide* showed no movements of this ship to Mexico or to the California coast during that time. Neither did the leading San Francisco paper take notice of any such visit. The ship did make the shipping news, however, with a pair of serious groundings in British Columbia, one in August of 1913 and the other in August of 1914.

Two other British-flag ships also made evacuation

runs in 1914, about which little is known. The steamer *Mexico City* (5,078/1896), registered in Hong Kong and considerably larger than the Canadian-based ships on the west coast of Mexico, brought 61 priests and 40 nuns to the United States after they had been expelled from Mexico. The 216-foot-long steamer *Acajutla* (1,170/1911) of Pacific Steam Navigation Company took refugees from Salina Cruz and the Isthmus of Tehuantepec south to the small Guatemalan port of San Jose.

To return to the better-documented events of that year, the prediction of war by the Mexican general at Manzanillo fortunately turned out to be as flawed as was his behaviour toward the evacuees aboard the *Cetriana*; no such war was to take place between Mexico and the United States. Soon, the wave of xenophobia waned, and the west coast of Mexico returned to whatever passed for normalcy in a country beset with revolution.

When war officially came to the area later in 1914, it was not a bilateral war between North American countries, but the First World War. As befitting ships and captains that had worked closely together within the past few months, the naval war between Great Britain and Germany was conducted on a very gentlemanly basis, at least initially.

The *Mexico City* - the British ship whose name the newspapers could not get straight - made at least two evacuation runs from the Mexican coast to California.

She was built as *Narrung*, owned originally by Wilhelm Lund and his Blue Anchor Line Ltd., and later by P & O. As *Mexico City* she returned to UK waters only to be

torpedoed off Holyhead by *U 101* on 5th February 1918. [*San Francisco Maritime National Historical Park*]

New roles for the *Cetriana*

Reflecting her freedom of movement, the *Cetriana* continued to get involved in unusual incidents. The bogus German consul had hit it off well with Captain Minister and stayed with the ship, and was still aboard her a few months later during her next adventure. At that time, August 1914, after the start of the war she served briefly as a collier for the German cruiser SMS *Leipzig*.

This curious situation came about because the German cruiser SMS *Nurnberg* had chartered the *Cetriana* several months earlier at Mazatlan to act as her collier, a perfectly natural relationship considering the mutual respect the naval officers and merchant captains of all the foreign nations had for each other. When the *Nurnberg* was rotated out of station-ship duty to join the fleet, the *Leipzig* came to Mazatlan. She inherited the charter, which meant that the *Cetriana* was duty-bound to follow the newly-arrived German cruiser.

The *Leipzig* left Mazatlan a few days before the start of the war and proceeded north up the coast toward California, followed by her faithful collier. By the time she arrived at Magdalena Bay in Baja California the war had begun; the cruiser then coaled for the final time from the *Cetriana*. The captain of the cruiser, who had both the right and the might to sink his British collier, gallantly gave the *Cetriana* her freedom, taking from her only the radio, which the Germans had installed during the charter, to ensure her silence. Captain Minister later expressed his appreciation for the way he had been treated by the cruiser captain.

The *Leipzig* had only a brief career as a raider before she was sunk at the Battle of the Falkland Islands early in 1915. However, during that time she captured and sank a few ships, including the British tanker *Elsinore* (6,542/1913) which she encountered off the mouth of the Gulf of California, en route in ballast from Corinto, Nicaragua, to Port San Luis in California. The captain and crew of this ship were dropped off at the Galapagos Islands where in time they found transportation to the South American mainland.

After the departure of the *Leipzig* there was little threat from German warships in the eastern Pacific. However, with the coming of war the British ships on the coast of Mexico had to step up their efforts to find cargoes. Commerce had already been badly interrupted by the revolution, sending shipping rates to a high level but simultaneously making cargoes scarce, forcing ship captains to be innovative in finding work for their vessels. In February 1915 the captain of the *Cetriana* saw a chance to pick up some salvage money in towing a disabled American freighter into Mazatlan.

His partner in this venture was the *Korrigan II*, the ship that had claimed the American sailing vessel as a prize at Manzanillo. At this point it was not perfectly clear which side of the revolution the *Korrigan II* was on since she was known to have changed sides under duress in 1915. Whether the salvage money was ever collected is not a matter of record, but at least the captain was able to continue steering a tight trackline between the two sides of the revolution.

Seizure of the *Cetriana*

Nevertheless, in May 1915 the *Cetriana* encountered a more serious crisis with Mexican authorities. At this point it is worth noting that not only did these officials tend to change sides in the revolution but, regardless of side, they tended to be pro-German and thus not inclined to give the benefit of the doubt to a British ship. On this occasion, however, the *Cetriana* was truly pushing her luck.

Upon the ship's arrival at Ensenada in Baja California the captain was detained and charged with smuggling, specifically in bringing in a group of Chinese and Hindu labourers. After authorities had denied the ship the right to land the aliens at Ensenada, the *Cetriana's* boats had been used to land the men surreptitiously on a nearby beach. When the captain was subsequently held incommunicado, along with his purser and radio officers, the Military Governor of Baja California accused the ship of leaving Mazatlan without proper clearance. A shipment

The Swan Hunter-built tanker *Elsinore* in the colours of C.T. Bowring and Co. Ltd. She was one of the few victims of SMS *Leipzig,* sunk on 11th Septtember 1914. *[Ian Rae collection]*

of gold aboard the vessel worth $140,000, some of it consigned in the name of the US Navy, may have also figured in the detention of the ship.

The British consul at Ensenada had reason for concern in as much as the military governor of Baja California was known to have separatist ideas, which meant if he were to establish his own government neither the Federal forces nor the revolutionaries in Mexico could exercise any control over his actions. The consul promptly called for a British cruiser, and soon HMS *Newcastle* was on her way from Central America. The American Navy also intervened by sending the cruiser USS *Denver* which became the first warship to reach the scene. The standoff ended quickly when the *Denver* towed the *Cetriana* out of Ensenada and all the way north to San Diego, an action that appeared to be a definite violation of the neutrality of the United States on several counts.

Wartime adventures of other British ships
The other Canadian ship also skirted trouble that year. After a voyage in June evacuating foreigners from Mazatlan the *Prince Albert* was chartered by Southwestern Steamship Company to take a cargo of arms to Topolobampo, a small port in the Gulf of California. This port was nominally under control of the Federalist forces, although Yaqui Indians and the remnants of Pancho Villa's army periodically raided the area, forcing the Federal troops to flee. However, *Prince Albert* was spared any risks of the revolution when she was stopped at San Pedro by customs officials who said the cargo was illegal contraband. Even though similar cargoes had been carried earlier by other ships, she was forced to unload and find another cargo.

During the remainder of the First World War a small number of British ships continued to work along the west coast of North America, particularly as additional ships came in after the opening of the Panama Canal in late 1914. Several were known to have fueled British or Japanese warships in American waters while the United States was still neutral, but these violations of the country's pro-British neutrality were generally overlooked. By the time that the United States entered the war in 1917 the Mexican revolution was largely over, so wartime evacuations, gun running, smuggling, and other such adventures became a thing of the past for British ships on the west coast of Mexico.

The aftermath
The *Cetriana* was sold to a firm in London, Cowasjee Dinshaw and Brothers who sent her out to their base in Aden to work down the east coast of Africa. Here, her luck as a survivor deserted her, and in July 1923 she sprang a leak off Kwayarina Island, Kenya and sank.

The *Prince Albert* also went on to other challenges. Following her railway service she became a rum-runner during prohibition in the United States, and finished out her days as the tug *J. R. Morgan.* She was broken up at Vancouver in 1949 at the age of 57.

No one could argue that the actions of these two ships from British Columbia, plus the two other British-flag ships, represented the finest hour of Britain's merchant navy. Nevertheless, one would have to concede that they provided some of the most interesting episodes that adventure-seeking readers could ever hope to relive vicariously with any ships.

NARRAGANSETT: AN EDWARDIAN SUPERTANKER
Colin Turner

In an age of VLCCs and ULCCs, a tanker with a deadweight capacity of 12,500 tons does not seem worthy of exciting the imagination. However, when such a vessel was completed on 5th May 1903, by Scott and Company of Greenock, she held claim to be the largest and most sophisticated oil tank steamer in the world. This remarkable ship was the *Narragansett*.

She was built for the Anglo-American Oil Company and was a development of the *Tuscarora* (6,117/1898). Like her precursor, the *Narragansett* was constructed with her engines amidships. Whilst it was already becoming customary for oil tankers to have their engines aft, this arrangement was considered by some naval architects to place too great a strain on the larger sized vessels when they were proceeding in ballast or experiencing heavy weather. Certainly, any decision to place the engines amidships would not have been taken lightly, for an article in the periodical *The Engineer* describes the extra expense attributed to building an oil-tight shaft tunnel throughout the after oil compartments.

With a gross tonnage of 9,196, the *Narragansett* measured 512 feet between perpendiculars (531 feet overall), with a beam of 63 feet 6 inches and depth of 42 feet. Her tanks could hold up to 11,000 tons of oil, in addition to which her bunkers could accommodate 1,500 tons. She was driven by a triple-expansion steam reciprocating engine (5,500 IHP) with cylinders of 31", 51" and 78" and a stroke of 60". On her trials this mighty engine produced an average speed of close on 13 knots in three double runs over the measured mile at Skelmorlie. For the purposes of her trials she was loaded down to her summer load-line.

Steam was generated under natural draught at 200 lbs per square inch in six single-ended boilers, that were placed three abreast in two stokeholds. The boilers burned coal at the outset, but were converted for the burning of oil fuel in 1909. The ship's funnel, which was her most distinctive feature, was 15 feet in diameter and extended to one hundred feet above the grate bars.

For discharging her oil cargo she was equipped with four 'Snow' type pumps, two in each of the forward and after pump rooms, which could discharge oil at a combined rate of 900 tons an hour. In this way she could discharge a full cargo in a little over 12 hours. A thorough installation of steam connections allowed for fire fighting and tank cleaning, whilst powerful fans were provided in both pump rooms to clear gas from the tanks.

Perhaps with the experiences of the Boer War so lately to mind, the *Narragansett* was so designed that she could, if required, be turned into an ordinary dry cargo steamer, although the 'tweendecks, which were well illuminated with portholes, could be utilised at any time for cargo and the carrying of troops or livestock. To cater for the loading and discharge of ordinary cargo, nine powerful winches and a series of 16 derricks on Samson posts were provided. The master, deck officers and engineers were also quartered in the 'tweendecks (alongside and forward of the engine casing) in accommodation that was described at the time as being 'remarkably comfortable and even lavish'. Provision for a small number of passengers was also included in this location. The seamen and firemen were berthed under the poop. All the accommodation was heated by steam and lit by electricity.

Although intended to transport oil primarily from ports on the United States' Atlantic seaboard, the possibility of voyages to Eastern waters was recognised in the ship's design. Her draught was limited to allow passage through the Suez Canal, and teak decks, extensive awning stanchions and good ventilation were provided for the comfort of the crew in hotter climates. The large number of awning stanchions can be seen on the accompanying trials photograph, but they were removed when the *Narragansett* came to be employed exclusively in the trans-Atlantic trade.

Thanks to her speed and fast discharge (her stays in port rarely lasted longer than 48 hours) she was able to exhibit some quick voyage times. On one occasion she completed a round voyage from the Tyne to New York, with a return to London, in 27 days.

It was during one of her Atlantic crossings in October 1913, that the *Narragansett* was instrumental in assisting in the saving of many lives from the burning emigrant liner *Volturno* (3,602/1902). Although a number of ships attended the stricken liner, heavy seas had hindered the rescue attempts. One lifeboat from the *Volturno* had already gone missing, whilst several others had been smashed on being launched. Boats from several steamers had managed to get alongside the burning ship, but the conditions were so bad that only a few passengers were snatched to safety. As night fell and the heavy weather showed no sign of abating, rescue attempts were suspended. It was Captain Barr of the *Carmania* (19,524/1905) who is credited with the idea of using oil to calm the seas and his radioed requests for a tanker brought the *Narragansett* to the scene. On her arrival she pumped thirty tons of heavy oil over the side and by this method the conditions were improved sufficiently to allow the rescue ships to transfer the surviving passengers and crew of the *Volturno*. In all 523 persons were rescued, but about 135 lost their lives in the early attempts to abandon the ship.

In May 1915, the *Narragansett* was on passage from Liverpool to Bayonne, New Jersey, when she picked up distress calls from the *Lusitania* (30,396/1907). Her master, Captain Charles Harwood, immediately laid a course to the position which had been given and worked the ship up to its maximum speed. The *Narragansett* had covered 22 miles of the 35 which had originally separated her from the *Lusitania* when a torpedo was observed heading for the ship. Fortunately it passed astern. The attacking submarine was the *U 20*, which had just dispatched the *Lusitania*. Her commander took his intended victim to be a Cunard freighter and remarked in his log that the torpedo had been defective. Captain Harwood resumed his passage fearing that the distress call had been a decoy to lure his ship into a trap.

The *Narragansett* was unable to continue to avoid such wartime perils and fell victim to a torpedo from *U 44* on the 16th March 1917, off South West Ireland, whilst on a passage from New York to Purfleet with lubricating oil. Admiralty radio had received two messages from the *Narragansett*, one carrying the information 'Arriving Purfleet Saturday' and, later, another saying '*Narragansett* sinking'. Her entire crew of 46 was lost with her.

Narragansett on trials in the Clyde. Note the ample provision of awnings. *[Glasgow University Archives]*

Two views of *Narragansett*, both believed to be at Avonmouth. The awnings have gone. *[Author's collection]*

DJAKARTA RAYA

Sun Shipbuilding Co., Chester, Pennsylvania; 1919, 8,739gt, 449 feet overall Four steam turbines geared to twin shafts by De Laval Steam Turbine Co., Trenton, New Jersey

Indonesia's first deep-sea shipping line, Djakarta Lloyd was established in 1951, two years after Indonesian independence and the company's first ships were somewhat elderly.

One was a 1918-built British standard 'G' type refrigerated ship, which was completed as White Star Line's *Gallic* and later sold to Clan Line as *Clan Colquhoun*. The other belonged to a remarkable group of sheer-less, flush-deck cargo ships with multiple masts which were instantly recognisable as belonging to the Luckenbach Steamship Company of New York, shipowners since 1889. These ships were ordered after the opening of the Panama Canal in 1914 and were designed for the East-West USA coastal trade, hence the large amount of cargo handling gear. One of a quartet ordered from the Sun shipyard, she was requisitioned on completion by the US Shipping Board, Philadelphia as *South Bend*. In 1923, she was bought by Luckenbach and renamed *J. L. Luckenbach* and remained in the fleet until 1948 when she was sold to the Republic Steam Ship Corporation, Panama as *San Francisco*. In 1951 Djakarta Lloyd became her new owner and she was renamed initially *Diponegoro* and then *Djakarta Raya* the following year. At the age of forty, she was sold to Hong Kong breakers in 1959. *[Fotoflite incorporating Skyfotos]*

230

GONE EAST
Peter Newall

Following the defeat of Japan in 1945, much of Asia was soon in turmoil as local inhabitants turned against their colonial rulers. The impact on the leading European shipping companies was serious as more and more Asian nationals started their own shipping lines, some of which are among the largest in the world today. In the early years, fleets were built up using second-hand tonnage and here is a selection of some of the interesting ships which saw out their twilight years in Eastern waters.

INDONESIA AND SINGAPORE

DJATIMULIA (top)
Arsenal de Brest, Brest; 1949, 8,267gt, 537 feet overall
Two 6-cyl. 2SCSA oil engines by Sulzer Compagnie de Construction Mécanique, Paris
After the Second World War, France set about rebuilding its devastated mercantile fleet. *Mékong* was the first in a trio of large, fast freighters built by French shipyards for Messageries Maritimes' Far East service. Originally ordered by Compagnie Générale Transatlantique as *Vancouver*, after the reorganisation of the French merchant marine in February 1948, she was allocated to Messageries Maritimes and completed as *Mékong*. In 1966, the two remaining sisters *Mékong* and *Meinam* (the third, *Peï-Ho* was wrecked in 1957) were sold to Djakarta Lloyd. In the end only *Mékong* flew the Indonesian flag as the deal to purchase *Meinam* fell through and she ended up in Hong Kong ownership. *Djatimulia* was broken up at Hamburg in 1971 whilst her sister continued in service for another six years before she too was scrapped. *[Peter Newall collection]*

KOTA SELANTAN (middle)
C. van der Giessen en Zonen's Scheepswerven N.V., Krimpen aan den Ijssel, 1939, 8,314gt, 476 feet overall
Two 8-cyl. 4SCSA oil engines by N.V. Werkspoor, Amsterdam
In 1946 the Straits Settlements were dissolved and Singapore became a separate crown colony. Full internal self-government followed in 1959 and, after a brief spell as part of the Federation of Malaysia, in 1965 Singapore became an independent state. Two years later one of the first Singapore-flagged shipping companies, Pacific International Lines (PIL), was founded by Y. C. Chang and among the initial vessels in the fleet were two famous Dutch cargo ships, *Straat Soenda* and *Straat Malakka*, which were completed before the war for Koninklijke Paketvaart-Maatschappij (KPM), Batavia. This unique pair was built for the Far East-South Africa route and had tall masts and a counter stern. Laid down as *Borneo*, *Straat Soenda* was almost lost in January 1942 when she went aground in the Soenda Straits with a valuable cargo of war goods. Refloated a week later, she spent the rest of the war years on charter to the Ministry of War Transport and was returned to her owners in 1946. In 1967 she was sold to PIL and renamed *Kota Selantan*. In May 1971, en route from Dar-es-Salaam to Mombasa, she struck a reef off Pemba Island and this time

she was declared a constructive total loss. *[Peter Newall collection]*

KOTA SENTOSA (bottom)
Barclay, Curle and Co. Ltd., Glasgow; 1950, 7,132gt, 485 feet overall
One 6-cyl 2SCSA Doxford-type oil engine by Barclay, Curle and Co. Ltd., Glasgow
Another well-known pair owned by Pacific International Lines were British India Steam Navigation's *Chindwara* and *Chantala*, bought in 1971. The third and fourth of nine 'C' class cargo liners built for British India between 1949 and 1952, *Chindwara* and *Chantala* were also the company's cadet ships, each capable of carrying up to twelve passengers and thirty one cadets. During their relatively short time with Pacific International Lines they were renamed *Kota Sentosa* and *Kota Aman* respectively and were broken up in 1974. *[Vic Young]*

231

SINGAPORE AND MALAYSIAN 'NATIONAL' CARRIERS

NEPTUNE AMBER (top)
Cammell Laird and Co. Ltd., Birkenhead; 1966, 5,345gt, 457 feet overall
6-cyl 2SCSA oil engine by Gebr. Sulzer A.G., Winterthur

The national carrier for Singapore is the Government-controlled Neptune Orient Lines which was founded in 1969. A year later they bought *Scotia*, which was one of a trio designed for Cunard Line's trans-Atlantic cargo service and the last traditional cargo ship built for the company - subsequent vessels were either bulkers or reefers. Although operated by Cunard, the three ships were in fact owned by a subsidiary of Cammell Laird. Redundant with the move to containerisation, *Scotia* was sold to Neptune Orient Lines in 1970 and was renamed *Neptune Amber*. In 1977 she was bought by Indian owners as *Sri Kailish* and in 1984, after two years of lay-up at Bombay, she was sold locally for scrap. *[Peter Newall collection]*

BUNGA BUTANG (middle)
Helsingborgs Varfs A/B, Helsingborg; 1948, 3,405gt, 341 feet overall
7-cyl 2SCSA oil engine by Burmeister & Wain, Copenhagen

In 1969, the same year as the establishment of Singapore's national carrier, a rival concern was founded in Malaysia, the Malaysian International Shipping Corporation. Although not government owned, the company is often seen as Malaysia's 'national' cargo line. In 1973 it bought this small ship for service in Eastern waters from the Norwegian company H.M. Wrangell of Haugesund and renamed her *Bunga Butang*. She was built in Norway as *Hoi Wong* for the Far East coastal trade, in which many Norwegian ships had operated before the war with Norwegian officers and Chinese crew. A 14-knot cargo ship, *Hoi Wong* was also designed to carry almost 1,000 unberthed passengers in 'tween deck space and on the weather deck. To cater for such large numbers, washrooms and galleys with rice boilers were provided in the two deckhouses and in the forecastle. In 1980 she was demolished at Singapore. *[Peter Newall]*

KUNAK (bottom)
N.V. Wilton-Fijenoord Sch. W. & Mach. Fabr., Schiedam; 1949, 4,513gt, 375 feet overall
8-cyl 4SCSA oil engine by Hawthorn Leslie and Co., Newcastle-on-Tyne.

Two companies seriously affected by the emergence of the new shipping lines in Indonesia, Singapore and Malaysia were the old colonial lines, the Singapore-based Straits Steamship Company and Koninklijke Paketvaart-Maatschappij (KPM) which was founded in 1891 and was the premier Dutch operator in the Dutch East Indies passenger and cargo trade. It is ironic, therefore, that this ship should be owned in turn by KPM, Straits and finally by the newcomer, Pacific International Lines. One of a series of small passenger ships built for KPM after the war, *Baud* had a capacity for over 2,000 deck passengers. For some reason, her Hawthorn Leslie engine was made in 1945 and only installed in *Baud* in 1949. In 1958 KPM moved their operational headquarters from Djakarta to Singapore and two years later *Baud* was sold to the Straits Steamship Company and renamed *Kunak*. Her final year before demolition at the hands of Pakistani breakers in 1978 was spent as PIL's *Kota Sari*. *[Peter Newall collection]*

DISTINCTIVE SHIPS

CHONGMING (opposite top)
S.A. Ansaldo, Genoa; 1941, 8,333gt, 473 feet overall
7-cyl 2SCDA oil engine by S.A. Fiat S.G.M., Turin

Italian naval architects have long been at the forefront of modern ship design and a perfect example is the quartet of cargo ships built in the early 1940s for the Genoese firm 'Garibaldi'. With their sleek appearance this group were years ahead of their time but unfortunately, because of the war, they have often been overlooked. Ordered for trading to South America and Central America, *Luciano Manara* was the second to be completed and the only one of the class to survive the conflict intact - two were later repaired after suffering serious damage. Used as a transport during the war, she was returned to her owners after the hostilities and was used as a tramp. In 1948 she was rebuilt as an emigrant/cargo ship with a capacity for 12 cabin passengers and 832 in steerage. After two unsuccessful migrant voyages to Australia, she was chartered in 1950-1951 by Sidarma Line for their emigrant service to Central America. Following the removal of her steerage accommodation,

232

she was renamed *Giuseppe Canepa* and was sold to Polish Ocean Lines in 1955 as *Malgorzata Fornalska*. Poland was one of the few countries with close ties to the People's Republic of China and, ten years later, she was sold to Chinese Ocean Shipping Company (COSCO), Peking and renamed *Chongming*. In 1979 she became *Hong Qi 144* (many coastal ships had this naming scheme which means *Red Flag 144)* and remained in *Lloyd's Register* until 1991. [A. Duncan]

EASTERN LION (middle)
Barclay, Curle and Co. Ltd., Glasgow; 1952, 7,651gt, 446 feet
4-cyl 2SCSA Doxford-type oil engine by Barclay, Curle and Co. Ltd., Glasgow
This distinctive cargo ship was once described as the 'tramp of the future'. Completed in 1952 as *Windsor* for the Britain Steamship Co. Ltd., London and managed by Watts, Watts, she was an evolution of the *Wanstead*-class (see *Record* 6) and her innovative design included hull knuckles for improved seaworthiness and excellent amidships accommodation for her crew. Three of this type were built and their design led to the ultimate Watts, Watts design, the *Weybridge*-class of 1958. Her career with Watts, Watts lasted less than ten years and in 1963 she was sold with one of her sisters, *Wokingham*, to a Bombay firm and renamed *Jag Ketu*. In 1967 she was bought by Lion International Co. Ltd., Hong Kong as *Eastern Lion* (seen here). After various changes of ownership, she became part of the Chinese Ocean Shipping Company, Peking fleet, her name unchanged. Although only deleted from *Lloyd's Register* in 1991, she was probably scrapped in the 1980s. [A. Duncan]

ORIENTAL AMIGA (bottom)
NV Wilton-Fijenoord Sch. W. & Mach. Fabr., Schiedam; 1950, 11,195gt, 498 feet overall
One set of double reduction geared steam turbines by General Electric Company, Erie, Pennsylvania
Another vessel which ended up in Hong Kong waters was Holland-America Line's *Diemerdyk* of 1950. She was designed for the Hamburg-North America West Coast passenger cargo service, which had been operated jointly with Royal Mail Line since the 1920s. With a passenger capacity of 61, like *Baud* the year before, her engines had also been made four years earlier. A sister, *Dinteldyk*, had been planned but during building was altered to a passenger ship, and completed in 1951 as *Ryndam*. In 1957 *Diemerdyk's* near sister, another *Dinteldyk*, was finally delivered for the West Coast route. In 1968 she was sold to C. Y. Tung's Oriental Africa Line and operated as *Oriental Amiga* on a round-the-world passenger cargo service with three former New Zealand Shipping Company passenger liners. Two years later she was joined by her former running mate *Dinteldyk* which became *Oriental Fantasia*. In 1971 she was converted into a containership and by the end of the decade both HAL ships had been sold to Taiwanese breakers. [Peter Newall collection]

CHINESE PUZZLES

ZHONG HUA (top)

With such a long coastline, it is not surprising that a number of ships sold to China have turned up again as Chinese coastal traders. This photograph of COSCO's *Zhong Hua* taken at Hong Kong is a real mystery. Obviously a Liberty converted to carry passengers but which one? In the late 1950s COSCO bought four Libertys, three of which had belonged to Bank Line: *Hong Qi 142 ex Springbank, Hong Qi 146 ex-Ericbank, Hong Qi 147 ex-Ninfea* (Italian) and *Zhan Dou 43 ex-Edenbank*. All were built at the Bethlehem-Fairfield Shipyard in Baltimore between 1943 and 1944 and were loaned to Britain during the war with *Sam* names. Apart from her name and owners, the only other known fact about this ship is that she was renamed *Ignacy Krasicki* and registered at Gdynia between 9th September and 7th October 1962 for a single voyage from Canton to Shanghai with a Polish crew. Was this to avoid requisition by the Taiwanese (Chinese Nationalist) Navy? She may also have been used to carry Chinese workers for the Tanzanian-Zambia railway. *[Peter Newall collection]*

LIU HAI 2 (middle)

Kockums M/V A/B, Malmö; 1942, 7,361gt, 445 feet overall
Two 6-cyl 2SCSA Sulzer-type oil engines by Kockums M/V A/B, Malmö

Another mystery is this ship photographed by Ted Scull at Shanghai in the late 1970s. One of the handsome group of twenty-one cargo ships with counter sterns built for Johnson Line between 1935 and 1948, three were sold to mainland Chinese breakers in the early 1970s: *Maco Venture ex-Peru, Maco Fidelity ex-Suecia*, and *Golden Wonder ex-Amazonas*. The most likely candidate may be the last mentioned which was illustrated on page 167 of *Record* 15, especially as her owner Guan Guan Shipping had a strong association with the People's Republic of China. Guan Guan bought *Amazonas* and a sister, *Orinoco*, from Johnson Line in 1964. It is also interesting to note that the former *Orinoco* as *Golden Spring* sank in November 1971 after striking a rock whilst approaching Shanghai! *[Ted Scull]*

ZHAN DOU 26 (opposite bottom)
*Todd-Bath Iron Shipbuilding Corporation,
Portland, Maine; 1942, 7,124gt, 442 feet
overall*
*T. 3-cyl. by General Machinery
Corporation, Hamilton, Ohio*
This vessel photographed in Shanghai
around the same time as *Liu Hai 2* was
probably one of the last operational
Ocean-type Second World War British
standard ships. Sixty Oceans were built in
the USA between 1941 and 1942 - half
came from the West Coast and the other
half from the Todd-Bath yard at Portland on
the East Coast. Completed as *Ocean
Merchant* in 1943, she and *Ocean Victory*
were sold to the Dutch Government in
London and placed under Dutch
management as *Jan Lievens* and *Jan
Steen*. In 1946 both ships were bought by
Reederij 'Amsterdam' and were its first
ships, *Amstelstad* and *Amstelveen* - this
company was formed as a tramping
subsidiary of Stoomvaart Maatschappij
Nederland and was SMN's first venture
outside the liner trade. *Amstelstad* was
sold in 1959 to COSCO and renamed *Ho*

Ping 26 and then *Zhan Dou 26* in 1967. As
she vanishes from reference books in the
mid 1980s, it is presumed she was
demolished around that time. *[Ted Scull]*

FORMER SCANDINAVIANS

ANITA (above)
*Akers M/V A/S, Oslo; 1928, 1,191gt, 253 feet
overall*
T. 3-cyl. by Akers M/V A/S, Oslo
Shown here during the 1960s in Hong Kong
and a long way from her original home, this
little ship was completed as *Bonn* in 1928
for Fred. Olsen's Jelø Line North Sea
services to German ports - Olsen had a
controlling interest in the Akers yard.
Bonn and her sister *Jelø* survived the war
and were sold for scrap in 1961. *Bonn* was,
however, resold to the Panamanian
Oriental Steam Ship Corporation, a
subsidiary of the Hong Kong firm
Wheelock, Marden and Co. Ltd. and as
Anita was chartered for two years' trading
in Indonesian waters. For some reason in
1966 she was seized at Saigon by the
Government of South Vietnam. After the

Vietnam War, with her name unchanged,
she was owned by the Government of the
Socialist Republic of Vietnam and was
probably scrapped during the 1980s if not
earlier. *[World Ship Photo Library]*

NGOMEI CHOU (below)
*Kockums M/V A/B, Malmö; 1949, 5,503gt,
464 feet overall*
*7-cyl 2SCDA M.A.N.-type oil engine by
Kockums M/V A/B, Malmö*
During the Second World War, Wilh.
Wilhelmsen, Tønsberg lost almost half its
fleet of 54 ships and from 1946-1954 a
major newbuilding programme took place
which resulted in 30 new motorships of the
type developed in the late-1930s but with a
split superstructure look which went back
to the early 1920s. With a service speed of
over 16 knots, *Trafalgar* remained in the
Wilhelmsen fleet for almost twenty-two
years and was sold in 1971 to Hong Kong
Atlantic Shipping Co. Ltd., Singapore and
renamed *Ngomei Chou*. Ownership was
later transferred to Hong Kong and she
was sold for scrap in Taiwan in 1978.
[Peter Newall collection]

FERNANDOEVERETT
Eriksberg M/V A/B, Göteborg; 1954, 4,432gt, 430 feet overall
6-cyl 2SCSA oil engine by Eriksberg M/V A/B, Göteborg

The Swedish-Levant Line was established in 1911 by Dan Broström and was the first Swedish line to operate to the Eastern Mediterranean. The name was later changed to Svenska Orient Linien or Swedish Orient Line. During the 1930s the company ordered a series of motorships from the Eriksberg Shipyard, Göteborg owned by the Broström group. *Vinterland* was the last of six 16.5 knot ships built by the yard between 1951 and 1954 - all with 'V' names, they were evolutions of the pre-war 'S' class with a long forecastle and compact centre-castle. Three were sold to the Philippines company, Everett-Orient Line, in 1968. The Everett family had been in the shipping business in Manila since the 1920s, and in 1955 they founded Everett-Orient Line which grew rapidly and, at its peak in 1980, the company had a sizeable fleet of almost thirty ships. *Vinterland* became *Fernandoeverett* and was sold to Kaohsi.ng breakers in 1979. *[Peter Newall collection]*

SECOND WORLD WAR US STANDARD SHIPS

PACIFICA (above)
California Shipbuilding Corporation, Los Angeles, 1943, 7,255gt, 442 feet overall
T.3-cyl. by Joshua Hendy Ironworks, Sunnyvale, California
Sixty-two Liberty ships were built as tankers. Outwardly, they looked like any other Liberty but with eight oil tanks they had a capacity of almost three million gallons. Completed as *John P. Altgeld*, this ship was sold in 1951 to Greek owners as the tanker *Androil*. Four years later, she was converted into a dry cargo ship at Nagasaki and lengthened to 512 feet. Lengthening of Liberty ships appears to have been a speciality of Japanese yards during the mid-1950s. Renamed *National Hope*, she was again sold in 1963 as *Kavala* and in 1967 her final sale was to Chinese Marine Investments Co. Ltd., Taipei who renamed her *Pacifica*. Two years later she was demolished at Kaohsiung. *[A. Duncan]*

ILIGAN BAY (below)
Pennsylvania Shipyards Inc., Beaumont; 1943, 5,203gt, 412 feet
Two 6-cyl 2SCSA oil engines by Nordberg Manufacturing Co., Milwaukee with electro-magnetic slip coupling and single-reduction gearing
Following her completion as a C1-A standard type, *Cape Arago* was bareboat chartered to the Norwegian Government and renamed *General Ruge*. After the war she was bought with another C1-A by Fred. Olsen to replace wartime losses and both were placed in service with a subsidiary, the Norwegian South America Line. As *Belgrano* she remained in the fleet until 1961 when she was sold to another Norwegian company and traded as *Strom Gunhild*. In 1968 she was bought by Universal Shipping Lines, Manila which was founded in 1965. As *Iligan Bay*, on 24th January 1971 bound from Antwerp to Manila with a crew of 39 and general cargo and chemicals, she sent a message reporting that the hatch cover to the rope locker had blown off during a gale off north west Spain. Nothing more was heard from the ship. Universal Shipping Lines was part of the Carlos A. Go Thong Lines group which continued to operate despite suffering a series of major shipping disasters including the loss of *Dona Paz* (2,324/1963) in 1987 - the world's worst-ever peacetime maritime disaster which resulted in 4,386 people losing their lives. *[Fotoflite incorporating Skyfotos]*

THE NORTH EASTERN REHEATED ENGINE

Several issues ago we challenged marine engineers (some of whom asked for more engine details in our captions) to tell non-engineers what the differences were between individual makes of triple-expansion engine, citing the reheat engine of the North Eastern Marine Engineering Co. Ltd. as an example. The following has been compiled from the rich harvest of letters, papers and diagrams submitted by readers, although especial thanks must go to Jack Winn for patiently answering the questions of a non-engineering editor.

The differences between steam engines from different manufacturers lay mainly in the design of such items as bedplates, columns and fittings. The last-named included a wide variety of items from reversing engines to air, bilge and general service pumps. However, towards the end of the steam engine's life, the North Eastern Marine Engineering Co. Ltd. (NEM) of Wallsend devised a way of increasing efficiency which in turn led to interesting divergences from the practice of other engine builders, especially in the matter of valves.

Superheating and reheating: the search for efficiency

The triple-expansion engine, with high-, intermediate-, and low-pressure cylinders, resulted from efforts to improve on the economy of the simple and compound steam engines. The addition of a superheater to raise the temperature of the steam to approximately 750°F before it entered the high pressure cylinder was a further important step in achieving economy, offering savings of 15% over an engine using saturated steam, largely through preventing steam condensing in the high-pressure cylinder. Even so, steam still condensed in the other cylinders, leading not only to loss of efficiency, but also to problems of leakage and wear in valves and glands. In addition, leaks meant water was lost, and had to be made up from the ship's fresh water supplies. As diesel-engine design developed, and began to demonstrate its potential to offer significant fuel savings over steam engines, the North Eastern Marine Engineering Co. Ltd. devised another refinement of the steam engine which offered meaningful economies: the reheat engine. The reheater was, essentially, a heat exchanger: it took the exhaust steam from the high-pressure cylinder, and passed it over a nest of 5/8-inch diameter tubes through which passed the main steam supply. As a result of this heat exchange, the temperature of the exhaust high pressure steam was raised from around 400°F to 580°F. The great advantage of this system was that the steam was 'dry' and thus condensation was avoided in the intermediate-pressure cylinder (IP, but shown as MP in the diagram opposite). In fact, the reheater ensured that steam entering the low-pressure cylinder was still hot enough to avoid condensation, and indeed the steam entering the condenser still had some degree of superheat. The reheater, which was a relatively straightforward device, achieved a saving in fuel consumption of 10% to 15% compared with a similar engine which had superheating only. If this sounds modest, it should be remembered that several hundred tons of coal would be burnt on an ocean voyage, and over the

life of such a robust engine (20 years could be confidently expected) the savings were very significant indeed. The downside, in addition to the higher initial cost of the reheater, was the requirement for a little extra maintenance.

Valve gear

The reheater engine had poppet valve gear on both the high pressure and intermediate pressure cylinders. Familiar from use in internal combustion engines, a poppet valve is one which lifts bodily from its seat, giving the advantages of quick opening and closing and a large port opening for a short travel. In contrast, a slide valve slides over faces incorporating steam inlet and exhaust valves, and a clack valve is secured at one point and opens only through a few degrees. Poppets were by no means novel, having been fitted to a large number of superheated engines by both NEM and rival engine builders. These valves were found particularly satisfactory in superheater and reheater applications, as they avoided exposing sliding surfaces to high-temperature steam.

Reference to the adjoining diagram is necessary to understand the subtleties of the poppet valve arrangements adopted by NEM, and which were superior to the others, according to correspondent Jack Winn. The trusted Stephenson link motion was used to drive a horizontally-mounted, semi-rotary shaft, to which were bolted four cam pieces. Two of these cams drove steam valves, and two drove exhaust valves. Having separate steam and exhaust valves reduced heat losses in a region where there was much turbulence, and also counteracted the deficiences of the Stephenson link motion when it was 'linked in'. This term referred to reducing the valve travel to decrease the cut-off, so that the steam was worked more expansively and hence more efficiently.

The cams actuated spring-loaded tappets which, in turn, lifted double-beat poppet valves. Double-beat valves have two seats placed one above the other, doubling the port area. On the NEM engine, the valve spindles were, of necessity, rather long, and were machined with annular grooves. As the steam made its way along the spindles, a certain amount of water condensed and settled in the grooves. This condensate prevented leakage and hence the valve stems needed no packing. In contrast, the valves in some other types of engines required packing top and bottom.

The radial vanes connecting the periphery of the valves to their centre bosses were offset and this meant that the steam gave them a rotary motion, so changing the

An NEM reheater in the flesh.

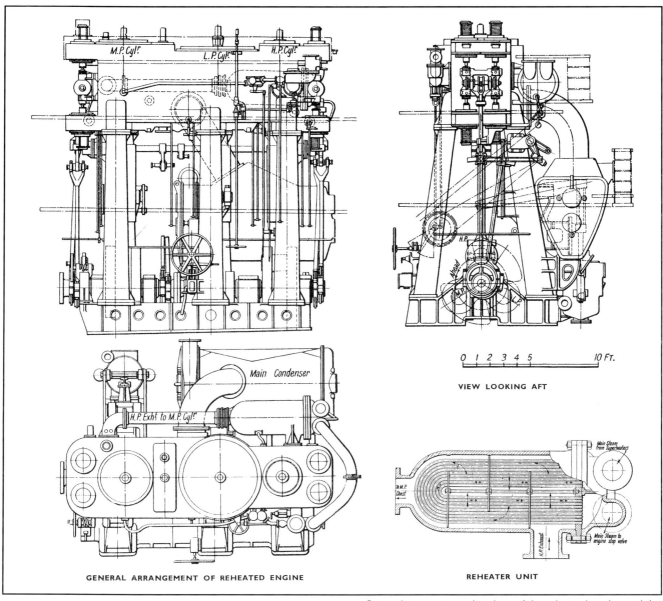

M.P. Cyl.   **L.P. Cyl.**   **H.P. Cyl.**

Main Condenser

H.P. Exht. to M.P. Cyl.

GENERAL ARRANGEMENT OF REHEATED ENGINE

0 1 2 3 4 5   10 Ft.

VIEW LOOKING AFT

Main Steam from Superheaters

To M.P. Chest

H.P Exhaust

Main Steam to engine stop valve

REHEATER UNIT

General arrangement drawings of the reheated engine and the reheater unit (above) and a section through the high-pressure cylinder and steam poppet valves (below).

seating at each opening. This reduced wear, as rotation of the valves minimised the problems of foreign matter settling on the valve seats. The valves were closed by springs which can be seen in the diagram, attached to the upper and lower extremes of the cylinder castings. The British Caprotti engine (more familiar from railway practice, although also developed for marine use) dispensed with these valves, and boiler pressure was utilised to close the valve - a simpler system

Because of the excellent performance of poppet valves with superheated steam, NEM chose to use them not just for the high-pressure cylinder but also for the intermediate-pressure cylinder of their reheated engine. To ensure the poppet gear was readily accessible, the low-pressure cylinder was moved to the centre of the engine. This arrangement of the cylinders also meant that thermal expansion was symmetrical, since the temperatures of the high and intermediate pressure cylinders were close.

Because steam was entering the low-pressure cylinder at a much reduced temperature, it did not require poppet valves, and slide valves sufficed.

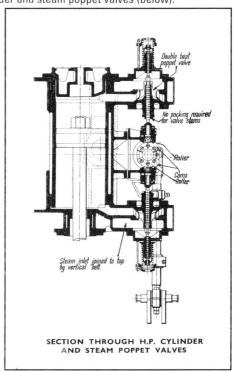

Double beat poppet valve

No packing required for valve stems

Roller

Cams
Roller

Steam inlet joined to top by vertical belt

SECTION THROUGH H.P. CYLINDER AND STEAM POPPET VALVES

First installation

An article in *The Shipbuilder and Marine Engine Builder* for May 1937 claims that North Eastern Marine Engineering Co. Ltd. reheated engines were first installed in the *Lowther Castle* (5,172/1937) and the *Lancaster Castle* (5,171/1937). This pair of cargo liners was built by Sir James Laing and Sons Ltd. of Sunderland for the Lancashire Shipping Co. Ltd., managed by James Chambers and Co. of Liverpool. On her maiden voyage, in ballast to the River Plate, the *Lowther Castle* achieved a particularly economical coal consumption, burning 17 tons per day for an average of 10.7 knots.

NEM patented their reheater system, but the reheater itself was not patented, as it was similar to other heat exchangers which were in use as feed water heaters. In further developments, NEM also introduced mechanical lubrication to the cylinders and valve chests and were about to introduce it throughout the engine, together with a totally enclosed crankcase, when development of this type of steam engine was abandoned in favour of the diesel engine.

Both the pioneer ships with reheater engines were victims of air attacks whilst in Arctic convoys. After being damaged at Murmansk on 24th March 1942, *Lancaster Castle* (above) was sunk by German aircraft when anchored in Murmansk Roads on 14th April 1942. There were nine casualties from her complement of 57.

Lowther Castle (below) was hit by aerial torpedoes 60 miles east south east of Bear Island on 27th May 1942 whilst on a voyage from Sunderland via Rekjavik to Murmansk in convoy PQ 16. Despite her blowing up the next day, her master was the only casualty amongst the 54 on board. *[National Maritime Museum P11529]*

THE PLENTY-STILL OIL ENGINE
Ken Garrett

Plenty and Son had been in operation at Newbury since 1790 making agricultural machinery and, later, steam engines. In 1912 they started to build Dutch Kromhout oil engines under license from J. Perman and Co. Ltd. of Bermondsey who held the UK agency. During the First World War much of the production space was taken up in making artillery shells. The company also tried to diversify and there was a project to build a commercial motor vehicle known as the 'Newbury Van'.

After the war the company set about designing their own oil engines that improved on the performance of the Kromhout units. These were still of the 'hot bulb' type known as semi-diesels. The introduction of the new engines was delayed for some months by a strike by the moulders and they did not come into production until 1920. Either because of the competition or the strike, Permans transferred the Kromhout license to Day, Summers and Co. Ltd. of Southampton. These were the smaller range of engines and much larger Kromhout units were being made by Kincaid and Co. Ltd. at Greenock.

In 1928, the oil engine section was split from the parent Plenty and Son and the Plenty-Still Oil Engine Co. Ltd. was formed. The company continued to develop and build their own oil engines but also became involved with the novel ideas of Dr. W.J. Still. Work on an experimental single-cylinder unit had been progressing at Newbury since 1926. Basically it was smaller version of the engine built by Scotts for Alfred Holt's *Dolius* of 1924 (see *Ships in Focus Blue Funnel Line*, page 71).

In 1927 an order for a three-cylinder unit was placed for the drift net fishing vessel *Larus* being built by Cochrane and Sons Ltd. at Selby. It had an ordinary reciprocating scavenge pump and a vertical, coal-fired Cochran boiler with an extra set of tubes to take the exhaust gases from the engine. This first production unit had the circulating water piped in circuit with the boiler and no shut-off valves were incorporated.

The camshaft for the steam poppet valves had three cams for each valve; starting, ahead and astern and a short cut off cam for normal running ahead. To obtain the changeover from one to another an elaborate system of gears and detents was designed with an eccentric shaft to lift the rockers clear. There was only one fuel pump driven by a large cam on the camshaft. This cam had three ramps and fuel was distributed to the appropriate injector through a steel block with three distribution valves and three spill valves to control the quantity.

Dr. Still and his manager, Mr. Acland, frequently visited the works during the building of the engine and many test hours were run. The design of the fuel injector nozzle gave a lot of trouble. The original design was called 'A' and they worked through the alphabet as far as 'U' with slight changes in the drilling of each nozzle. Eventually, the variation known as 'T' was chosen. The engine was shipped to Selby in January 1928. The *Larus* was completed just before Easter and sailed to Lowestoft to pick up her fishing gear before proceeding to her intended fishing grounds in the Irish Sea, for which she was based at Milford Haven. Fishing for herring, she was

out for three or four days at a time but returned to Milford with more mackerel in her hold than anything else.

At first all seemed to be going well but towards Whitsun she began to get slower and slower and the cylinder heads were removed so that the pistons could be examined. It was found that the penetration of the fuel spray from the injector nozzles was too long and the pistons were developing pits in their crowns. The piston combustion rings were renewed and the engine boxed up again. The vessel went back to the fishing grounds but, when trying to return to Milford some days later, the engine refused to start and she had to be towed 80 miles into port by the steam drifter *Plumer* (LT 596). It seems that steam had been passing the lower rings and entering the upper combustion chambers. These rings had not been disturbed during the previous examination. At this stage somebody appears to have called a halt to the experiment. The ship was taken out of service and after a few months the machinery was removed and replaced with something more conventional.

So the project failed. The fruits of success would have given fuel economy and enabled the steam below the piston to start the engine and eliminate the need for air compressors and storage bottles. However, the fundamental difficulties could not be overcome. This flirtation with the Still principle probably held back the development of a cold-start, solid-injection diesel engine at Newbury for several years.

The company failed in 1931 and the works closed. By this time a number of ships owned by F.T. Everard and Sons Ltd. had Plenty engines and they were very concerned at the failure of the engine builders and the consequent lack of spare parts. In the autumn of 1932 Everards purchased the company and the Newbury Diesel Co. Ltd. was formed. But that is another story.

As far as I can ascertain, the first marine application of a Still engine was in an experimental vessel, apparently named *Meccano*, built by Dennys of Dumbarton in 1917. The engine itself was built by Savery of Birmingham, possibly with assistance from Denny. The engine was removed after two years. Other companies who took out licences to build the Still engines were Scotts of Greenock, Peter Brotherhood Ltd. of Peterborough, Kitson and Co. Ltd. of Leeds who built an experimental steam locomotive, and Dujardin of Lille in France.

Edgar Wildsmith, who worked on the engine in the workshop at Newbury and also went to sea with the *Larus* as the guarantee engineer, related much of this information to me. He had served his apprenticeship at Newbury and later spent a year at sea as fifth engineer on the new *Baron Dalmeny* (3,536/1924). He recalled seeing the *Dolius*, I think in Port Said, undergoing some major engine repairs on an early voyage. The problem was apparently due to some valves in the line between the cylinder water jackets and the boiler having been inadvertently closed. He understood that the valves had been fitted at the insistence of the classification society or the Board of Trade.

The only application of the Plenty-Still engine was in the drifter *Larus* (101/1929 LT 381 - upper photograph). But it was short-lived and in 1929 *Larus* was sold to Arthur G. Catchpole, and towed to Lowestoft. Here the Plenty-Still engine was taken out and its casing incorporated into a conventional triple-expansion engine by Elliot and Garrood of Beccles. Renamed *Silver Crest* (LT 46 lower photograph), the drifter fished successfully for many years, although her career was punctuated in October 1939 when requisitioned by the Admiralty as a minesweeper. Returned to commercial fishing in 1945, she was joint winner of the 1956 Prunier Trophy, landing 215 crans of herrings at Lowestoft on 22nd October 1956, earning £1,700. At the end of a long and honourable career, she left Lowestoft on 2nd November 1960 for Bruges and breaking up. *[Top: K. Garrett collection; bottom: B.G. Banham collection]*

Original Scott-Still combined steam and diesel engines are shown opposite. Top is the starboard engine for Holt's *Dolius* (5,996/1924) on a test bed, the boiler being seen to the upper left. An experimental single-cylinder Scott-Still engine is seen to the extreme left. Below is what is probably the starboard engine, part of the larger installation for the *Eurybates* (6,280/1928). *[Both: Glasgow University Archives GD323/3/131/520/2 and GD323/3/13/1/533/5]*

243

PUTTING THE RECORD STRAIGHT

Letters, additions, amendments and photographs relating to articles in any issues of *Record* are welcomed. Letters may be lightly edited.

Points from 14

Having just completed reading *Record* 14 (and an excellent edition it was), just a few comments for possible inclusion.

To be strictly correct the location for *Pacific Enterprise* (page 73) is not Liverpool but Birkenhead Docks - Cavendish Quay, West Float - with Gilbrook Basin to the extreme right of the shot - where the grain barges are berthed alongside Rank's Ocean Flour Mill. The 87-ton capacity sheer legs just ahead of the *Pacific Enterprise's* bridge appear to have been used for loading/unloading at least three heavy lifts on deck alongside numbers 2 and 3 holds. One wonders are these gun turrets for or from a naval vessel? The sheer legs survived into the 1970s and were often used for loading new propellers emanating from the Stone Manganese works in Wallasey, but are, alas, now no more.

The Monks Ferry Coaling Jetty (page 113) still survives, I am pleased to relate, although not surprisingly all of the railway track and loading equipment has long since disappeared. Being made of sandstone, it is quite a substantial structure and can still be accessed by the public from the new waterfront promenade at Birkenhead (via Ivy Street). I believe it was last utilised as a coaling jetty in August 1961, by which time the number of coal-fired steamships on the Mersey was rapidly declining. It was operated by Rea Ltd., owners of the well-known barge and associated tug fleets on the Mersey. The railway connection that served it from the Birkenhead Joint main line at Blackpool Street, Birkenhead survived serving Monk's Ferry Civil Engineer's Depot until official closure on 20th July 1966. Although berthing alongside the jetty is now expressly forbidden (so proclaim a number of notices affixed thereto) a number of small boat owners use it to embark and land fishing parties during the summer months because of its incline - it is available at almost any state of the tide.

The venerable *Janis Rainis* (page 120) was certainly in service beyond 1967 - I photographed her discharging on South Kings No. 1 Branch Dock, Liverpool in August 1968 - and she still looked in remarkably good external condition then! The white waterline had gone - she was sporting plain green boot topping.
NIGEL BOWKER, Poulton Green Close, Spital, Bebington, Wirral, Merseyside CH63 9FS.

Plural *Urals*

I have to say that I disagree with John Hill's interpretation of the information in *Lloyd's Registers, Lloyd's Confidential Index* and *Lloyd's Shipping Index (Record* 15). The part about the first *Ural* is correct. However, the second seagoing *Ural* of 1934 - deleted from *Lloyd's Register* in 1936 - is in my opinion a phantom ship. She is either a re-entry of the first *Ural* of 1932, or a vessel which was completed under another name. A check of a posted 1935 *Lloyd's Register* should show which. There is no evidence to support such a tanker serving in the Soviet Navy - a vessel of that size would have been much too large for the needs of the Navy at that time and certainly could not have escaped the attention of *Jane's Fighting Ships*. The rounded-off gross tonnage of 6,100 is a give away- she was not a completed ship.

The *Ural* in the photo in *Record* is identical to the ship in my photo collection and to a negative in my collection, taken at Rotterdam on 18th August 1966. I contend that the *Ural*, initially listed as built in 1956, based on the date she was rebuilt, is one and the same as the ship listed from about 1964, first as undated then as built in 1934. The identical gross tonnage (6,377) is given in *Lloyd's Shipping Index* of 25th March 1963 for her (then shown as built 1956), and in *Lloyd's Shipping Index* of 7th December 1964 (shown without a building date). This vessel is noted as trading as early as 1960 in *Lloyd's Shipping Index* and last appears trading foreign in 1969.

When thinking about products of Soviet shipbuilding it is a good idea to think about Five Year Plans. Soviet shipbuilding has always operated in terms of series production, not one-offs. The Soviets already had a standard tanker design of about 8,000 gross tons in production beginning in 1953 - so they would not have produced a one-off tanker of similar size. I would not be absolutely sure that the 1934 building date is exact - it may have resulted from a valiant effort by a clerk at Lloyd's Register to square a circle by reference to the phantom ship dropped from the 1936 *Register*. I think, given the propulsion plant, it is most likely she is a rebuilt Caspian Sea tanker, but it is also possible she is the result of the marriage of a salvaged Second World War wreck and surplus machinery. But any way you cut it - the vessel listed as built in 1956 and the vessel listed from 1965 onwards as built in 1934 are one and the same.

During the nineteenth and early twentieth century many ships were built for the Caspian Sea in European shipyards (U.K., Germany, Belgium, Sweden) and delivered via the Baltic Sea and a river and canal route to the Volga River and the Caspian Sea. This same route was used to bring tankers out from the Caspian for use as naval oilers in the Baltic during the First World War. With the completion of the Volga-Don Canal in the Soviet period (and its subsequent enlargement), it was possible to bring large Caspian Sea tankers in light condition out to the Black Sea. In addition to the possible *Ural*, there are three more which were trading in the Black Sea, Mediterranean and beyond in the mid-1960s: *Agamali Ogly* (1930), *Sumgait* (1934), *Azerbaidjan* (ex-*Beria*) (1935). Assuming the *Ural* to be a rebuilding, the other three were somewhat less modified for ocean service - the most striking visual difference being that the midship structure is quite open at the main deck level.
BILL SCHELL, 334 South Street, Holbrook, Massachusetts, USA

John Hill replies as follows.
I am not surprised that, given the confusion arising from entries in *Lloyd's Register*, and *Lloyd' Confidential Index*, there is ample scope for different interpretations, and I appreciate Bill Schell's views.

After further studying the records I have at home, I can give some ground to Bill, but I must disagree with his contention that *Ural* (2) was a phantom ship. You will recall that the *Motor Ship*, in two separate entries about two years apart, referred to the building of two tankers of different tonnage, each of which started life as *Ural*; the first of which was renamed *Josif Stalin* almost immediately. However, the 1932 ship was very much alive under various, names, until broken up in 1971.

In stating that the second *Ural* of 1934 was deleted from the *Register* after one year, I was careful to say that she *probably* entered 'Soviet Government Service', - not the Soviet Navy service - as I too could find no mention of the ship in *Janes' Fighting Ships*. As Bill suggests, perhaps a posted copy of the 1935 *Lloyd's Register* would indicate why the ship was deleted - *Lloyd's Register* would not normally delete an almost new ship without a good reason. Otherwise, the career of the *Ural* (2), between 1935 and the early 1960s will have to remain a mystery.

When *Ural* (2) reappeared in the 1960s, the 1932 *Ural* (1) was still to be found in the Register as the *Nicolaev*, so there was no 'phantom' about one, or other of these ships!

Turning now to *Ural* (3), I agree with Bill but suggest that this really was a 'phantom' ship. Bill is quite correct to point out the similarity in dimensions between *Ural* (2) and the *Ural* (3) and I am now inclined to believe that there was never a new *Ural* (3) built in 1956. Rather, I venture to suggest that *Lloyd's Register* got it completely wrong and that what was listed as *Ural* (3) was, in fact, a re-engined and partially rebuilt *Ural* (2). If this interpretation is correct, one has to accept that the erroneous entry in the *Register*, concerning the 1956 built *Ural* went undetected for the 25 years from 1956 until 1981.

To conclude, I believe that I was correct in stating that

the picture in *Record* 14 was of the *Ural* of 1934. But the existence of a *Ural* (3) was a red herring - as was your caption.
JOHN B. HILL, The Hollies, Wall, Hexham, Northumberland NE46 4EQ.
Unfortunately, the posted Lloyd's Register *for 1935* gives no clue as to why *Ural* was deleted. Ed.

Golden Grace, and how Port Adelaide got her goalpost

The photos of *Goldens Bear* and *Wonder* on page 171 of *Record* 15 are recorded as having been taken by Alwyn McMillan on 4th June 1991 - the very day I transferred from the latter ship to the former. From the company launch crossing Singapore's Eastern Working Anchorage, I noticed the *Golden Bear* had just acquired that shameful excrescence, a deck electricity generator (under the bridge, starboard side so not shown on your shot). One of her four engine room M.A.N. alternators had given up the ghost and this was the only viable alternative to keep within Lloyd's requirements. Despite our engineers' valiant efforts, that 'deck jenny' never did work satisfactorily - wrong cycles - but a brand new Mitsubishi job replaced the defunct one in the engine room when we got up to Shanghai three months later. This one worked splendidly. To display a jenny on deck is an insult to your engineers - an open suggestion to all that they cannot make their mighty motors go properly! The deck jenny went ashore as soon as the Mitsubishi was on line.

To complete the Guan Guan Hall of Fame I enclose a shot I took of their last ship - appropriately named *Golden Grace*, as she completed discharging her urea cargo at the lovely little East Malaysian port of Sandakan on 21st November 1996. Incidentally, the excellent photos of some of those older ships clearly show the broad yellow band on the black-topped blue funnel. This was a feature of the ships running only from Singapore to Australia.

Bill Laxon's Port Line comments on page 181 of *Record* 15 are very interesting, as is his photo of the magnificent *Port Brisbane*. Deep laden for home, she has just pulled off the wharf (Wellington?) and my guess is she will now anchor and put overside the punt enabling the lads to paint out those horrible dirty rubbing marks (caused by lying alongside port side to the quay) ready for the long run home in pristine Port Line condition.

James Pottinger asks about the *Port Adelaide's* mast - how did it come to change from the pole mast of her builder's plans, to the latter day goalposts-with-topmast? Upon her completion by Hawthorn Leslie, at Hebburn-on-Tyne, the owners decided the pole mast would not suitably carry the required cargo derricks and asked the builders to come up with an improvement. So, soon afterwards, my uncle - a draughtsman at the yard - was given this task and he, with his brother (my father who was also a draughtsman) designed the goal post mast on the back of an envelope during their weekly Friday evening in the 'Gibraltar Rock' in Tynemouth, over their usual modest couple of half pints.

Uncle Tom, of course, checked the calculations and drafted the new design properly in the drawing office on Monday morning, the new mast was soon made and shipped to replace the original. My life-long pal Mike Hatton happened to be her fourth mate so of course knew this true story - and for the rest of *Port Adelaide's* life she was known on the Australian and New Zealand waterfronts as 'the ship which was designed in a pub!'

CAPTAIN A.W. KINGHORN, 15 Kendal Avenue, Cullercoats, North Shields, Tyne and Wear NE30 3AQ
Sadly, whilst compiling this issue, we heard that Alwyn McMillan died on 1st April 2001.

With reference to the letter in *Record* 15 on the change of a single mast to a goalpost in *Port Adelaide*, the original mast was vibrating itself to pieces and it had to be changed. *Port Adelaide* loaded out from New York on her maiden voyage in June 1951 and she was listed to take the January sailing from London in 1952 but was replaced by *Port Wellington* so she may have returned to the shipyard then for the matter to be dealt with.
IAN FARQUHAR, RD2, Dunedin, New Zealand

Lamports and Liver Birds

Rowan Hackman in his excellent article about the Lamport and Holt 'Vs' states that a possible cause of the loss of the *Vestris* was striking floating wreckage. I have to hand a copy of the abridged report of the inquiry into the loss, published by the *Journal of Commerce*. Nowhere in this is there any reference to contact with flotsam being a possible cause of the ingress of water into the ship.

In its judgement the court found that the main causes of the vessel capsizing were:
1. Overloading. The *Vestris* was overloaded by 7.25 inches when she left the berth at Hoboken. This represented 400 tons deadweight.
2. Deficient stability. The *Vestris* was a 'tender' ship and on this occasion had too small a margin of stability and reserve of buoyancy.
3. Leaks from the starboard ash ejector, the 'bobby' hatch (sic) on the shelter dock and through the shipside half doors on the upperdeck.
4. Failure by the crew to batten down bunker hatches early enough, if at all, thereby allowing water to enter the coal bunkers saturating the coal, causing the list and probably thus causing the clogging of the pump suctions.
5. Failure by the crew to plug the starboard scuppers after the vessel had taken a list. This resulted in more water coming on board through these scuppers after the discharge outlets were submerged.
6. Lack of wing suctions in ballast tanks.

It had been the practice for vessels on the service to leave the berth overloaded. *Vestris* had done so on at least one previous occasion as had *Vauban*. The reason for this was that the ships could only leave the berth at slack water and waiting until the vessel was correctly trimmed could have resulted in the loss of a tide and a delay of up to six hours. The ships were supposed to anchor in the lower part of New York harbour and pump out ballast water until they were at the correct draught. This practice was illegal under British law but not, seemingly, at that time, under US law. There is no mention of *Vestris* having anchored to pump out ballast after leaving the berth. This illegal practice had been the subject of correspondence between the Board of Trade and Lamport and Holt in 1926.

The *Vestris* was a shelterdeck ship. This meant that, even though the bunker hatches were inside the superstructure, they were weather deck hatches and were required to be battened

Guan Guan's last ship, the *Golden Grace* (10,889/1977) at Sandakan, Malaysia on 21st November 1996. She became *Santa Suria* in 1998 and is still listed in *Lloyd's Register* for 2000-2001 in the ownership of Bendera Mawar Sendirian Berhad of Malaysia. *[Captain A.W. Kinghorn]*

down at sea. The half doors opened on to a cross alleyway and there were two bunker hatches in this alleyway. Water taken through these hatches could flow down to the boiler room and the 'tween deck bunkers. There was evidence from the ship's Chief Officer to the effect that there were no covers provided for these hatches although other witnesses disputed this.

Although the company had an assistant Marine Superintendent in New York he was paid through the local agents, Sanderson and Co., who were, in effect, the ships' managers. The ships maintaining the service seldom visited the UK, and therefore all drydockings and surveys were carried out in New York. The ships were rarely if ever seen by Board of Trade surveyors; for instance, *Vestris* had not visited the U.K. since 1921. Lloyd's and the US authorities carried out all surveys.

After sailing from New York on the Saturday afternoon the weather had deteriorated. The wind and sea were on the port quarter making steering very difficult and by noon on the following day water was already entering the stokehold. On the Sunday evening the ship was struck by two exceptionally large waves which caused her to roll heavily to starboard. After this the starboard list was substantially increased. Some of the cargo also shifted, further increasing the list. The ship foundered on Monday 12th November 1928.

The fleet list states that *Vestris* was on a voyage from London and New York to Buenos Aires at the time of her loss. This should be New York to Buenos Aires, as she had not called at a UK port since 1921.

With regard to the photograph on page 152, I think that it is highly unlikely that this was taken in January unless it was at Buenos Aires. Some of the people in the picture are wearing straw hats and none have overcoats: hardly the dress for Liverpool or New York in mid-January! I think that the *Vestris* is alongside the Prince's Landing Stage in the picture and the dress of the people on the stage is more suited to September. But, if this is her maiden voyage, why is the ship not dressed overall? According to Noel Bonsor in *South Atlantic Seaway*, the *Vestris* did not return to Liverpool after her first voyage to Buenos Aires but entered the service to New York, sailing from Buenos Aires on 26th October 1912. For her to be in Liverpool on 9th January 1913 she would have to have completed a round trip to New York, turned around at Buenos Aires and returned to Liverpool in 75 days: quite a tight schedule! Unless, of course, she returned to Liverpool direct from New York which is unlikely.
GEOFF HOLMES, 17 Bayswater Court, Newport Avenue, Wallasey, Wirral, Cheshire CH45 8QJ

On page 153 of *Record* 15, in the caption to the photos of *Voltaire*, I see a comment about the flag being flown ending with 'There must be a story to this'. I'm surprised at you! I should have thought that there would be a synopsis of the story, with that superior little suffix -'Ed', which alludes, of course to said Editor's omniscience. On page 48 of *Mercantile Houseflags and Funnels*, there are brief details, on which I shall expand slightly.

In 1966 I first noticed a Lamport and Holt vessel flying as a stem jack a blue flag with the arms of the City of Liverpool in a white ball at the centre. I wrote to Lamports and received a reply saying that their ships were the only ones with the privilege of flying the civic flag of the City of Liverpool while in port in Liverpool. This honour was given in the early 1930s by Miss Beaver, then Lord Mayor, in recognition of the services of the passenger ships *Voltaire* and *Vandyck*, which were then engaged in cruising from Liverpool to European ports, thus giving employment to many Liverpudlians during the recession. I note that *Voltaire* is flying the flag from the foremast, as well as at the jackstaff. By the time I became familiar with Lamport ships, the custom seemed to be that of flying the flag solely as a stem jack. Perhaps this was because most of their ships were of typical Vestey Group build, with only the foremast having a topmast, and the yard-arm being fully occupied with houseflag, pilot flag and other signals. Incidentally, the fact that the L and the H on the company's houseflag were connected by a plus sign rather

than an ampersand, was alleged to be indicative of the relationship between William James Lamport and George Holt. Be that as it may, it didn't stop seamen saying the initials stood for 'Lean and Hungry'.
J.L. LOUGHRAN, 333 Streetsbrook Road, Solihull, West Midlands B91 1RW
Thanks also to Craig Carter for details of the custom of flying the Liverpool civic flag. Ed.

Hull in the Hundreds
A few comments which I hope will be helpful on a great selection of photos.
Cluden: 'Steel' in the third column becomes 'Smith' (twice). A transposition from Smith-Hughes, perhaps?
Carpathian: I think her sale to British Petroleum was in June 1917, a year earlier than you say.
Exmouth: It was not the Depression that shortened her life. She stranded near Brighton on 12th November 1929. After refloating, she was condemned as a constructive total loss and sold to T.W. Ward Ltd. who broke her up at Grays in January 1930.
Dartmouth: I don't think any question arises of Goulds being 'allowed' to rename her. There were no restrictions on renaming in 1915; that came later, I think in 1917. In contrast, renaming restrictions were imposed much sooner in the Second World War.
Queensland: The Kish family was also involved as shipbuilders at Sunderland from 1882 to 1884 as Kish, Boolds and Co.
BILL LAXON, Waimarana, Upper Whangateau Road, PO Box 171, Matakana 1240, New Zealand.

Annings' origins
The 'Hull in the Hundreds' article in *Record* 15 shows two Anning steamers, *Exmouth* and *Dartmouth*. In the text accompanying the photographs, reference is made to the Anning family as being Appledore men. My River Exe notes seem to show that they came from Starcross on the River Exe, in south Devon. Their first vessel was the new schooner *Experiment* (built Topsham 1826, 117 tons (old) and 95 tons (new) measurement). Captain William Anning and Thomas, a yeoman, bought 16/64th and 8/64th shares respectively. By 1837, Captains William and John, plus Thomas, owned all 64 shares. In 1853 48/64th passed to an Exmouth man and John retained his 16/64th until his death in 1858, when his widow Susanna took over the shares which she held until the vessel was lost on the Dutch coast in October 1862. From 1826 the family owned, either wholly or in part, a total of 13 sailing vessels. Their earlier vessels were generally employed in the home trade but they soon began trading further afield - Baltic and Mediterranean and then West Indies and South Africa. John Henry Anning sold his interests in their last two sailing vessels in 1879 and 1880, respectively *Jessie Anning* (built Bridport, 292/1865) and *Ann Wheaton* (built Bridport, 228/1865). In the meanwhile, the family had begun steam operations in 1876 with the *Richard Anning* (built Dixon, Middlesbrough, 1,132/1876) followed by the *Henry Anning* (Palmer, Jarrow, 1,650/1878). They owned a total of 13 steamers which were given either family names or those of South Devon towns and villages.
MARTIN BENN, 5 Grove Road, Walton le Dale, Preston, Lancashire PR5 4AJ

Just had *Record* 15, and particularly enjoyed the lovely tramp steamer shots in the 'Hull in the Hundreds' feature. However, I must 'set the record straight' - and it's my fault, not yours! My claim in *Cardiff Shipowners* that the Annings came from Appledore has since been proved incorrect - they were from across Devon, from Exmouth to be precise, hence other ships' names such as *Dawlish* and *Starcross*. So I'd be glad if you published a 'sackcloth and ashes' note from me in the next *Record*.
Dr. DAVID JENKINS, National Museums and Galleries in Wales, Department of Industry, The Collections Centre, Heol Crochendy, Parc Nantgarw CF15 7QT

Was *Tamele* a standard?

The photograph of *Tamele* on page 166 of *Record* 15 gives rise to several comments.

Firstly, the accommodation block does indeed look small for the number of passengers which the *Tamele* carried and the explanation for this observation can be derived from a statement in the *Motor Ship* of April 1945: 'Under present conditions 36 passengers are carried in 12 three-berth cabins, but each of these will be arranged for one person in normal trading'.

Similar arrangements for temporary increased passenger accommodation were to be found in many of the larger cargo liners built during the Second World War under private contract; e.g. the Royal Mail 'D' class refrigerated ships and the standard fast cargo ships ordered by the Ministry of War Transport in 1942.

In the case of the *Tamele* and her 'running mate' in the Liverpool to West African intermediate passenger service, the *Tarkwa*, the cramped wartime passenger accommodation was retained until the two ships were disposed of, presumably because there was a requirement for cheaper accommodation than the mail boats could offer.

Regarding my second query, I have always wondered if the *Tamele* was designed by Elder Dempster, or was a Cammell Laird inspired type of fast cargo liner. I think the latter, because she was followed at Birkenhead by a sister ship, the *Sacramento*, which was delivered to Ellerman's Wilson Line. Had the *Tamele* been specifically built to Elder Dempster's requirements, one would have thought that this company would have met their needs for a second ship by taking the *Sacramento* (which must have been on the stocks when the *Tamele* entered service), rather than purchasing the *Tarkwa* from the Caledon Shipbuilding Co. Ltd. at Dundee.

The *Tarkwa* differed from the *Tamele* in many respects and was rather obviously a modified Blue Funnel design, not unlike the *Telemachus*, which had been built by Caledon the previous year (1943).

Reverting to the Cammell Laird ships, the *Shipbuilder* in 1945, described the *Sacramento* as 'being built to a standard design of the Ministry of War Transport.' If the *Tamele* and *Sacramento* were a standard type, it seems odd that no further ships of this design were built, by Cammell Laird or elsewhere. Alternatively, could Cammell Laird have produced the design themselves with a view to marketing it as a replacement for liner tonnage lost in the Second World War? If this was the case, the shipyard was not very successful.

JOHN B. HILL, The Hollies, Wall, Hexham, Northumberland NE46 4EQ

Swansea tug identified

The tug on page 56 of *Ships in Focus Blue Funnel Line* (referred to on page 180 of *Record* 15 by J.W. Grainger) is the *Nora* (99/1899) owned in the early 1920s by the West Coast Towage and Salvage Co. Ltd. (J. Prendiville and Co., managers), Liverpool, whose funnel she sports.

JOHN BARTLETT, 6 Cottenham Park Road, London SW20 0RZ

Facts for 15

Kim Ann, ex-*Timor* did not come to an unknown end (*Record* 15, page 165). *Lloyd's Annual Return* for 1984 says she was broken up at Huangpu (Whampoa).

The second *Margaret Rose* (ex-*Pavlova* of 1912) was acquired by Skogland and re-named *Morna*. She began a conversion to dry cargo, but this was never completed - I do not believe she ever fished under Norwegian flag (page 177).

Brazilian Prince (page 178) is a Hildebrand photograph copied several times over - she was outbound from Boston but during one of the copyings somebody reversed her direction.

At the start of the Hansen list, the German name of *Hubbastone* was *Jürgensby*. In 1943 she was put under management of J. Jost, Flensburg. German sources give her loss as sunk 24th June 1943, north of Cape Arkona, cause unknown.

BILL SCHELL, 334 South Franklin Street, Holbrook, Massachusetts 02343, USA

When SMS became KMS

On page 150 of *Record* 15 the listing for the *Vandyck* states she was captured by the German auxiliary cruiser SMS *Karlsruhe* whereas she was a fleet light cruiser built by Germania Dockyard at Kiel. On page 153 the *Voltaire* is shown as being sunk in action with the SMS *Thor* on 4th April 1941. This should, of course, be

Although taken from a very different angle from the shot of *Golden City* ex-*Tamele* in *Record* 15, this view of *Sacramento* (7,096/1945) shows they were sisters, albeit with detail differences, especially to the topmasts. Although nominally owned by Ellerman's Wilson Line Ltd., *Sacramento* here flies Ellerman and Bucknall's houseflag, and she was formally transferred to this associate company in May 1964, shortly afterwards becoming *City of Bristol*. She was sold in 1969, becoming first *Felicie* and in 1971 *30 de Noviembre* in the Cuban fleet, returning to the UK for demolition at Faslane in July 1977. A photograph of *Sacramento* in the late John Harrower's *Wilson Line* (World Ship Society, Gravesend, 1998) shows her with extra lifeboats on the deckhouse athwart the second mast. *[World Ship Photo Library]*

the KMS *Thor*. SMS stands for Seiner Majestät Schiff, which ceased use on the death of the Kaiser. KMS stands for Kriegsmarine Schiffe.

On page 143 the two photo captions have been reversed. The NMM photograph is the bottom one and further research has been done on this image. It shows the *Hermanos* entering Montevideo, probably on 3rd January 1913. The only time the *Hermanos* was at Montevideo throughout the 1905-1914 period was in 1913 when she arrived on 3rd January from Mobile and sailed on 12th March for Pensacola. John Naylon's article says she became the *Dova Rio* in 1911 but this is not correct. David Hodge has checked the *Lloyd's Weekly Shipping Index* and the issue for 19th February 1914 gives *Hermanos* - to be renamed *Dova Rio*. The *LWSI* for 19th March 1914 gives *Hermanos* - now *Dova Rio* which see. She sailed from Gulfport for Rio de Janeiro on 4th March and it is likely that the renaming took place at Gulfport.

Once again a splendid edition.

R G TODD, Head, Historic Photographs and Ship Plans Section, National Maritime Museum, Greenwich, London SE10 9N17

Additions to past editions

I have just been back through my old issues of *Record* and have come up with a few comments which might tie up some loose ends.

Away back in *Records* 1 and 2, there was some discussion about the motorship *Tolten/Glenearn* and the exact nature of its ownership in its rather confused early history *(she resurfaced in* Record *15 - ed)*. Glen Line agreed to purchase *Tolten* from Lithgows by an agreement dated 29th June 1933. The purchase price specified in the agreement was £120,000 payable on 22nd September 1934, and Lithgows did indeed hold a mortgage to secure the price. In the interim, no interest was payable *per se*, but Glen operated the vessel on payment of a monthly sum of £1,467 4s 8d of which £100 was regarded as part payment of the purchase price. Under the agreement, Glen had certain rights to cancel the transaction, in which case the monthly payments were forfeited.

The reconstruction plan for Glen Line following the Royal Mail collapse (dated June 1934) was drawn up on the basis of Glen cancelling the transaction, but *Glenearn* carried on sailing for Glen until the end of her sixth voyage on 3rd December 1935. Of these voyages, only the last was truly successful in terms of profit, and on one *Glenearn* actually made a loss of £589. I have not yet discovered whether the original 'hire-purchase' agreement was extended, or whether the price was actually paid and the ship resold later.

On another Glen Line matter, this time regarding the series of articles on whale-ship conversions, one of the company's vessels nearly ended up as potential subject matter. In early 1929 Glen received an offer of £85,000 for their 1915-built *Gleniffer*, a sister of *Cardiganshire/Salvestria*, from an un-named party interested in converting her to a whaling ship. The offer was attractive, as *Gleniffer* then stood on Glen's books at £50,000, but was turned down on the grounds 'that at such a figure no similar vessel of the same specification can be acquired and the sale would disorganise the service'. Until Holts rescued Glen in the mid 1930s, the company had no money for new construction: hence the *Glenearn/Tolten* saga.

In a more recent issue, *Wellington Star* (*Record* 9, page 26) was not in convoy when sunk by *U 101* on 16th June 1940. A ship of her speed would have proceeded independently under most circumstances, and she was indeed unescorted when sunk. Most of her complement were picked up by the French motor ship *Pierre L.D.* (5,795/1935), and one lifeboat reached land on its own. *Auckland Star* was also sailing independently when sunk by *U 99* a month later and all of her crew made land safely in the boats. While I have not checked actual survivors' reports, I would suspect that both of these large new vessels sank quite slowly in good weather conditions, allowing safe evacuation.

With regard to the 'Swans on the Lakes' article in *Record* 12, some further details on *Winona* (page 247) might be of interest. She was actually one of a number of lakers brought across the Atlantic by a tonnage-hungry British Government. She was due to sail in Convoy SC 7 on 5th October 1940, but had to turn back very early with engine trouble and thus missed the massacre of that convoy as it neared its destination. She sailed again with SC 8 on 15th October. Two other lakers, *Eaglescliffe Hall* and *Trevisa*, also sailed with SC 7. Both straggled in bad weather, and the latter was sunk by *U 124* on 16th October (actually the first ship sunk from the convoy). Both *Winona* and *Eaglescliffe Hall* served in the D-Day armada in June 1944. There is an Imperial War Museum photograph of *Winona* on D-Day service in John de S. Winser's *The D-Day Ships* (World Ship Society, Gravesend, 1994).

The history of the *Stirling Castle* (*Record* 15, page 172) is actually even more interesting than you think. In 1885, two years after her sale to Bruzzo and renaming as *Nord America*, she was actually sold again to British interests. The purchaser was J.W. Adamson of London, and she was re-registered under the British flag at Malta under her original name of *Stirling Castle*. I suspect this was a speculative purchase to take account of the Government's need for fast tonnage during an international crisis, and she was indeed chartered to the Government. She appears as *Stirling Castle* under Adamson's name in *Lloyd's Register* for one year. With the crisis and the charter over, Adamson resold her back to Bruzzo and she reverted to *Nord America*. In subsequent *Lloyd's Registers*, she appears as *Nord America* (ex-*Stirling Castle*, ex-*Nord America*, ex-*Stirling Castle*). This is probably the source of Bonsor's comment that she carried both names during her Italian career. Incidentally, the statement that she was reduced to one funnel is incorrect. Bonsor actually says '...her two funnels replaced by longer and thinner ones' - and the photo on the opposite page of *North Atlantic Seaway* (volume 3, page 1267) actually shows her with the new funnels.

Dr MALCOLM COOPER, Flat 5, Leonard Court, 68 Westbourne Terrace, London W2 3UF

On pronouns

Record 14 was the accustomed delight. I was particularly taken by the article on Australian two-funnellers (more Antipodean material would be welcome at any time), but as usual there was very much that was of interest, Richard Pryde's feature on Soviet shipping being a good instance.

What a pity, therefore, that the pleasure of the latter article was slightly marred by Mr. Pryde's insistence on using the pronoun *it* to refer to the ships featured in it. In half-a-century of talking to seafaring folk, I have never once heard any of them refer to a ship as anything other than *she*, and would maintain that this is therefore the only correct usage in this context; obviously one is used to hearing it from those who know nothing about ships (such as television journalists), but then it is simply a mistake born of ignorance, rather like referring to the funnel as the chimney. Mr. Pryde is clearly very far from ignorant, and so one is drawn to wonder just why he has done as he has.

Only two possible explanations occur to me. The first is that he perceives the use of *she* for a ship as an anomaly, in that English refers to all other inanimate objects as *it*, and that that somehow makes him uneasy. Well, he is entirely correct about its status as an anomaly, but I can assure him I speak here as a professional linguist that it is no cause for unease: languages were not designed by committees, nor do they operate according to the canons of logic. They are, as a consequence, full of anomalies: one has only to consider the verb *to be*. It's deeply anomalous, but I would hope that Mr. Pryde would not consider that any reason to regularize it and go around saying I be; you be; he bes.... The very fact that the verb *to be* is so irregular is testimony to its extreme importance, for it is a linguistic axiom that the more important a thing is, the more likely it is that the words referring to it will be irregular. It is perhaps unsurprising, then, given the transcendental importance of ships in the history of the English-speaking peoples, that the language should harbour an anomaly in the shape of the pronoun used to refer to them.

The second possibility, it seems to me, is that Mr. Pryde has been on the receiving end of just such a tirade as that which I once received from a feminist friend when, in the course of

As a follow up to the photograph of the *Nadir* on page 157 of *Record* 15, Alex Duncan sent this 1950 photograph of the ship under her previous name of *Atlantic Star* (7,160/1945) in Livanos ownership at Cape Town. Alex points out that her bridge structure is standard for a Fort and Park, as are her ventilators, and suggests that the Turkish owner of *Nadir* may have altered the superstructure, perhaps to give him space to live on board. He confirms that crews of timber ships laden like *Nadir* certainly did have to scramble over deck cargo to work the ship. *[Alex Duncan]*

driving along Dublin's North Quay, I happened to comment on a vessel that we were passing, to which I referred (of course) as *she*. I was roundly assured by our friend that she resented being compared to a ship (whether she was philosophically or aesthetically justified in that resentment is fuel for a different argument) and that I ought henceforth to do women the favour of calling ships it.

Well now, I'm far from lacking in sympathy for the feminist cause (I've fought for equal rights all my life), but I have never done our friend's bidding, solely and simply because she was mistaken in her reasoning. It is, patently, true that we refer to a woman and a ship alike as *she*, but this does not connote a comparison or any connection whatsoever between the two. We also refer to both a cockroach and the Taj Mahal as *it*, but we are not comparing the latter to the former, or even vice versa. By the same token, although those who have any cause to speak of me use the same pronoun for the purpose as they do when talking about Hitler, namely *he*, I take no offence at the fact, and don't infer that they are trying to equate the one of us with the other.

It is sad, therefore, that Mr. Pryde thinks that he has to part company with the rest of us in this matter. It obviously goes against the grain with him, and occasionally he forgets himself and comes out with the likes of '...her true fate being unknown' (of the *Kara*, page 121). I should like to think that I may have

demonstrated to him that there is no good reason, linguistically or logically, for him to persist in his strange practice, and that he can return to the use of *she*, with which he will doubtless feel much more comfortable.

CHRISTY MAC HALE, 142 Moscow Drive, Liverpool L13 7DL

The editor admits that he too has strayed from the paths of righteousness and on occasion failed to call a ship she, feeling mightily uncomfortable when the vessel carries a name which is undeniably masculine, such as John Johnasson *(Record 15, page 183).*

David Eeles has looked in local newspapers for details of the casualty to John Johnasson *in Torquay harbour illustrated in* Record 15, *page 183. It was reported that she had arrived from Kings Lynn with 780 tons of coal, and that a south easterly gale had worked her against the seaward side of South Pier, starting leaks and causing her to flood. After unloading, which was somewhat impeded by her sinking, she was pumped out by a salvage tug, and it was found that damage was mainly to her side. The newspaper reports state that she was brought into the inner harbour, and made ready to be taken to Plymouth for survey. Not surprisingly given her 37 years of age, repair was not economic, and she was broken up at Dunkirk.*

SOURCES AND ACKNOWLEDGEMENTS

Photographs are from the collection of John Clarkson unless otherwise credited. We thank all who gave permission for their photographs to be used, and for help in finding photographs are particularly grateful to David Whiteside and Tony Smith of the World Ship Photo Library; to Ian Farquhar, Bill Laxon, Peter Newall, Ivor Rooke, William Schell, George Scott; to David Hodge and Bob Todd of the National Maritime Museum; Dr. David Jenkins of the Welsh Industrial and Maritime Museum; and other museums and institutions listed.

Research sources have included the *Registers* of William Schell and Tony Starke, *Lloyd's Register, Lloyd's Confidential Index, Lloyd's War Losses, Mercantile Navy Lists,* and *Marine News.* Use of the facilities of the World Ship Society's Central Record, the Guildhall Library, the Public Record Office and Lloyd's Register of Shipping are gratefully acknowledged. Particular thanks also to William Schell and John Bartlett for various information, to Rowan Hackman for yard numbers and launch dates, to Heather Fenton for editorial and indexing work, and to Marion Clarkson for accountancy services.

Harrison four masters
Haws D. *Merchant Fleets 15, Thos. & Jas. Harrison* TCL Publications, Hereford 1988 was initially consulted to arrange the ships into classes, with biographical details being confirmed from the sources listed above.

MacLagan diesel
In addition to the sources cited in the text, information came from Barclay Curle archives, University of Glasgow.

Narragansett: Edwardian supertanker
The Engineer, 20th February 1903 and 15th May 1903.
Dunn L. *The World's Tankers* A. Coles, Southampton, 1956.
Mitchell WH and Sawyer LA. *Sailing Ship to Supertanker* Terence Dalton, Lavenham, 1987
Cowper C. 'Burning of the Volturno' *Sea Breezes,* June, 1963.
Mielke O. *Disaster at Sea.*
Hoehling AA and M. *Last Voyage of the Lusitania.*

Gone East
Many thanks to Bill Schell and Maurizio Eliseo for their help with US and Italian shipping information.

The North Eastern reheated engine
Correspondents who contributed were Jack Winn, Alec Hopper, Bill Lind, C.J. Moore, Tony Morton, Brian Smith and Bernard Teale.
'Verbal Notes and sketches for marine engineering officers', compiled by Southern's Marine Engineering College, Glasgow; James Munro and Co. Ltd., Glasgow.
'The Reheated Reciprocating Marine Steam Engine', paper presented to the Institution of Naval Architects by Harry Hunter on 7th April 1938.
'The Lancaster Castle: a Wear-built General Cargo Carrier fitted with new North Eastern Reheated Triple-expansion Machinery' *The Shipbuilder and Marine Engine Builder,* May 1937.

The Plenty-Still oil engine
As well as sources cited, the author discussed the Still engine and many other matters concerning the various Newbury engines with Peter J. Humphreys who was the Managing Director of the Newbury Diesel Co. Ltd. until he retired in 1987. Thanks to Barry Banham for details of *Larus.*

Albert White and his compound steam engine
'The White Combined Steam Engine', paper presented to the Institute of Marine Engineers by Albert White on 13th April 1937.
Clarke JF. *Building Ships on the North East Coast*
Jenkins JG. *Evan Thomas Radcliffe - a Cardiff Shipowning Company* National Museum of Wales, Cardiff, 1982
Heaton PM *The South American Saint Line* Starling Press, Risca, 1985.
Jenkins JG and Jenkins D. *Cardiff Shipowners* National Museum of Wales, Cardiff, 1986
Middlemiss N. *Travels of the Tramps Volume III* Shields Publications, Newcastle, 1992.

ALBERT WHITE AND HIS COMPOUND STEAM ENGINE
John B. Hill

Since the advent of steam propulsion marine engineers have been looking for means by which to improve reliability and enhance the efficiency of their machines. The severe economic depression of the 1930s provided ample inducement to Albert White to search for ways in which the economy of the traditional steam-engined tramp ship might be enhanced, without compromising the proven reliability of the simple reciprocating engine, with its coal-fired Scotch boilers.

Albert White's ideas were to prove attractive to a number of shipowners, resulting in his design being specified for some fourteen cargo ships and one trawler. Had it not been for the outbreak of hostilities and White's untimely death in 1940, his Combined Engine might well have been more widely adopted, but the exigencies of war, and the urgent necessity to replace lost tonnage, dictated that only the simplest of machinery would be manufactured during the emergency, efficiency being a secondary consideration.

White and oil firing

William Albert White was born at Sunderland in 1878 and after an apprenticeship at Middle Docks, South Shields, he saw sea service as a marine engineer. In 1904 White was appointed as the guarantee chief engineer of the Tyne-built, Canadian lakes steamer *Turbinia*, the first turbine-engined merchant ship to cross the Atlantic. Then, having developed a particular interest in turbine machinery, White went on to find shore employment as a supervisor at a New York factory which manufactured Parsons-type steam turbines. Returning to England during the First World War, White became interested in the use of oil fuel for marine boilers and he patented the White oil-burning system, which was widely used for many years.

Initially establishing a marine engine works at South Shields, White later moved to Hebburn. About this time he acquired the marine engineering interests of J.P. Rennoldson, with a view to constructing ships' propulsion machinery at the new premises of the White's Marine Engineering Co. Ltd.

White's new engine

In the early 1930s Albert White applied himself to the design of a new type of ship's machinery, of fairly modest power, but with improved economy, which he hoped would be attractive to tramp-ship owners. His ambition was to produce the maximum power possible from the steam generated by conventional oil- or coal-fired boilers. White was of the opinion that only well-tried equipment should be used. There would be no new principles involved, and maintenance would be within the capabilities of engineers currently employed on board conventional cargo steamers.

Instead of a traditional triple-expansion engine, which usually operated at a speed of about 60-70 rpm, a high-speed, totally enclosed, steam engine would be used, with speed-reduction gearing; output being supplemented by a low-pressure exhaust turbine, connected to the main

engine gearbox. The new engine would be of the double-compound type (i.e. with two high-pressure and two low-pressure cylinders), with a totally enclosed crankcase, operating at a speed of 500 rpm. Although an innovation for tramp steamers, the double-compound engine had been in use for a number of years, principally on board German and Scandinavian ships.

The employment of reduction gearing was something new, but the same type of gearbox had given satisfactory service for several years in German cargo ships, which had twin diesel engines geared to a single propeller shaft.

The choice of main engine was favoured because its well-balanced crankshaft would reduce the risk of damage to the gear teeth and also because it would produce a more uniform flow of exhaust steam to the low pressure turbine. Other features which White included in his quest for maximum efficiency were the use of superheated steam and two stages of steam re-heating, firstly after the high-pressure cylinders and then before the low-pressure turbine.

Surprisingly, the result was a relatively easily-operated power plant; although rather more sophisticated than was usually associated with tramp ships. There would be some additional steam piping in the engine room, but nothing which would add to maintenance requirements, and there was the estimated 40% saving in fuel consumption to be considered.

Applying the White-engine

In collaboration with the engine works of Hawthorn, Leslie and Co., an experimental engine of 500 HP, together with a specially-designed exhaust steam turbine, were assembled on a test bed at the St. Peters Works and subjected to extensive trials.

Favourable results encouraged White to look for a ship in which to prove his ideas afloat. For this purpose he established the White Shipping Co. Ltd., and purchased the Lamport and Holt turbine steamer *Boswell*, which had been built at Belfast in 1920. Renamed *Adderstone*, her turbine engines were removed and replaced with a set of the new combined steam machinery. Whites claims were sufficiently well demonstrated in service, to the extent that a new cargo ship was ordered from Short Brothers, Sunderland, to further illustrate the efficiency of the new machinery.

The second ship of the White Shipping Co. Ltd., the *Biddlestone*, entered service in 1937, but by that time a number of South Wales shipowners, namely the South American Saint Line, Evan Thomas, Radcliffe and the E.R. Management Co. Ltd., had been attracted to the new, economy engine and had placed orders for a total of eleven steamers, all of which were to be built at the Sunderland shipyards of J.L. Thompson and Bartram and Sons Ltd.

With a view to extending the application of the White engine, a 270-ton trawler was ordered by White Trawlers Ltd. from John Lewis and Sons, Aberdeen in 1935. Into its hull was fitted the original 500 horsepower

The first vessel to be fitted with a White engine is seen here in three guises. Above, she is Lamport and Holt's turbine-driven *Boswell* which was purchased in 1933 to be fitted with a White engine. In 1934 she emerged as *Adderstone* and the photograph to the right may well have been taken when she first sailed from the Tyne with her new machinery. After a spell under the Norwegian flag she was sold to Japan in 1951 to become *Norway Maru*, as which she is seen below at Adelaide. Under this name she was fitted with a diesel engine in 1958, but she appears to be unmodified in this shot. Her original White engine gave a creditable 24 years' service. *[Top: A. Duncan; middle: George Scott collection; bottom J. Y. Freeman]*

test engine. Although no more trawlers were to be propelled by White engines, the *White Pioneer* (renamed *Mary White* in 1937) retained her original machinery for 13 years, including six years in Admiralty service as a boom-defence vessel.

Excluding the trawler, fourteen White-engined ships were in service when the Second World War commenced (see accompanying list), but no less than nine of them were to be victims of enemy action.

The engine in service

In the few years between delivery and the outbreak of war, the technical press spoke favourably about the performance of the White engine. A saving in fuel consumption of about 30% was acknowledged and, whilst this was challenged in some quarters, there is no doubt that the economy of the machinery compared favourably with that of contemporary triple- and quadruple-expansion steam engines. On the other hand, a degree of complication involving additional items of equipment has to be admitted. A few early first-hand accounts of operating the machinery have come to light and all are favourable, notwithstanding the use of superheated steam, but one wonders if reliability was maintained as the ships aged?

It is of interest to note that, of the five ships which survived the war, three were re-engined and one had its White double-compound engine renewed. The small trawler engine lasted until 1947, when it was replaced with a conventional triple-expansion engine.

It has not been possible to trace any senior engineers who had extended first-hand experience of operating the White engine, but there have been hints from deck officers that the ships were underpowered, difficult to manoeuvre in adverse weather conditions, and barely able to maintain a speed of 10 knots. This could be why some of the ships were re-engined, but it does not explain why interest in the White Combined Engine did not revive in post-war years.

White's death in 1940 and the growth in popularity of the diesel engine were probably significant factors.

The life and protracted death of the trawler fitted with the original White test engine is shown on these pages. This page top, she is *White Pioneer* as built, and as renamed *Mary White* in 1937 (middle and bottom). The opposite page shows her end, wrecked as *Luffness* at Aberdeen in January 1958 (upper) and awaiting scuttling off Girdleness in April 1958 (lower). *[This page top: George Scott collection; others Tony Lofthouse collection]*

SHIPS FITTED WITH WHITE ENGINES
Shown in chronological order of completion

1. ADDERSTONE
O.N. 143686 5,327g 3,169n 400.4 x 52.4 x 28.4 feet
1934: 5,255g 3,116n
Two steam turbines geared to one shaft by Harland and Wolff Ltd., Belfast; 538 NHP, 2,300 IHP, 10½ knots.
3.1934: C. 4 cyl. by White's Marine Engineering Co. Ltd., Hebburn-on-Tyne with low-pressure turbine; 460 NHP, 2,000 BHP, 11 knots.
1958: Fitted with 6-cyl. 2SCSA oil engine made by the Niigata Engine Co. Ltd., Niigata, Japan.
1.7.1920: Launched by Harland and Wolff Ltd., Belfast (Yard No. 550) for The Shipping Controller, London as WAR BAMBOO.
2.11.1920: Registered in the ownership of the Liverpool, Brazil and River Plate Steam Navigation Co. Ltd. (Lamport and Holt Ltd., managers), Liverpool as BOSWELL.
19.11.1920: Completed.
30.5.1933: Acquired by the White Shipping Co. Ltd. (Robert I. James, manager), Hebburn-on-Tyne.
10.2.1934: Renamed ADDERSTONE.
4.1937: Sold to Skibs A/S Germa (John Gerrard, manager), Kristiansand, Norway and renamed GERMA.
1950: Sold to Wah Mow Hong (Wallem and Co., managers), Hong Kong and registered in Panama.
4.1951: Sold to Daiichi Kisen K.K., Kobe, Japan and renamed NORWAY MARU.
1960: Owners became Daiichi Chuo K.K., Kobe.
1965: Owners became Daiichi Sempaku K.K., Kobe.
1967: Sold to Fujita Kaiji Kogyo K.K., Osaka, Japan.
5.2.1970: Demolition began at Tadotsu, Japan, and was completed by 1.4.1970. She had been laid up at Kawajiri, Hiroshima since December 1968.

2. WHITE PIONEER
O.N. 161586 270g 118n 126.3 x 23.2 x 12.6 feet
C. 2-cyl. by White's Marine Engineering Co. Ltd., Hebburn-on-Tyne with low-pressure turbine; 96 NHP.
1948: T. 3-cyl. by A. Hall and Co. Ltd., Aberdeen; 86 NHP.

1.8.1935: Launched by John Lewis and Sons, Aberdeen (Yard No. 134).
9.1935: Completed for White Trawlers Ltd., Hebburn-on-Tyne as WHITE PIONEER (NE 3).
1937: Renamed MARY WHITE (NE 3).
1.1940: Requisitioned by the Admiralty for use as a boom defence vessel, pennant no. Z 147.
1943: Sold to Shire Trawlers Ltd. (W.A. Bennett, manager), London
2.1946: Returned to owners, fishing number GY 465.
12.1948: Sold to Newhaven Trawling Co. Ltd. (W. Carnie junior, manager), Granton.
1949: Renamed LUFFNESS (GN 57).
21.1.1958: Driven ashore on the North Pier, Aberdeen and subsequently grounded. Later handed over to Metal Industries (Salvage) Ltd. for removal.
15.4.1958: Refloated and towed to position 57.5 north by 2.1 west off Girdleness to be scuttled.

3. ST. HELENA
O.N. 162140 4,313g 2,605n 399.0 x 56.0 x 22.3 feet
C. 4-cyl. by White's Marine Engineering Co. Ltd., Hebburn-on-Tyne with low-pressure turbine; 304 NHP, 1,468 IHP, 10 knots.
8.4.1936: Launched by J.L. Thompson and Sons Ltd., Sunderland (Yard No. 573).
3.7.1936: Completed.
1936: Registered in the ownership of the St. Quentin Shipping Co. Ltd. (B. and S. Shipping Co. Ltd., managers), Newport as ST. HELENA
12.4.1941: Torpedoed by the German submarine U 124 off Freetown in position 07.50 north by 14 west whilst on a voyage from Montevideo and Bahia to Hull with a cargo of grain and general, including canned meat, cotton, rice and hides. The crew of 38 was saved.
23.4.1941: Register closed.

The first 'production' vessel to be fitted with a White engine was the *St. Helena. [John B. Hill collection]*

254

4. ST. MARGARET
O.N. 162141 4,312g 2,604n 399.0 x 56.0 x 22.3 feet
C. 4-cyl. by White's Marine Engineering Co. Ltd., Hebburn-on-Tyne with low-pressure turbine; 304 NHP, 1,530 BHP, 1,650 IHP, 11 knots.
22.5.1936: Launched by J.L. Thompson and Sons Ltd., Sunderland (Yard No. 574).
8.1936: Completed.
17.8.1936: Registered in the ownership of the St. Quentin Shipping Co. Ltd. (B. and S. Shipping Co. Ltd., managers), Newport as ST. MARGARET.
27.2.1943: Torpedoed by the German submarine U 66 in position 27.38 north by 43.23 west whilst on a voyage from Liverpool to Pernambuco and Buenos Aires with general cargo and coal. Three of the 50 on board were lost, and the master taken prisoner.
25.4.1943: Register closed.

5. ST. CLEARS
O.N. 162142 4,312g 2,604n 399.0 x 56.0 x 22.3 feet
C. 4-cyl. by White's Marine Engineering Co. Ltd., Hebburn-on-Tyne with low-pressure turbine; 304 NHP,

1,460 BHP, 1,620 IHP, 11 knots.
4.1947: C. 4-cyl. made in 1944 by White's Marine Engineering Co. Ltd., Hebburn-on-Tyne with low-pressure turbine.
7.7.1936: Launched by J.L. Thompson and Sons Ltd., Sunderland (Yard No. 575).
9.1936: Completed.
22.9.1936: Registered in the ownership of the Barry Shipping Co. Ltd. (B. and S. Shipping Co. Ltd., managers), Newport as ST. CLEARS.
4.4.1939: Owners became the South American Saint Line Ltd. (B. and S. Shipping Co. Ltd., managers), Newport.
10.1951: Sold to F.L. Nimtz, Hamburg, Germany.
12.1951: Renamed KONSUL NIMTZ.
12.1959: Sold to the Pan Norse Steamship Co. S.A., Panama (Sun Wha Shipping Co, and later the New China Steamship Co., beneficial owners) (Wallem and Co. Ltd., Hong Kong, managers) and renamed NORELG.
1.9.1962: Driven ashore on the east coast of Ma Sze Chau Island, Tolo Harbour, Hong Kong during Typhoon Wanda.
12.1962: Wreck sold to Patt, Manfield and Co. Ltd.
18.12.1962: Breaking up began.

Of the five 'Saints' fitted with White engines, three were to become war losses. *St. Margaret* (upper photograph) was torpedoed in mid-Atlantic in February 1943, whilst proceeding independently after her convoy dispersed. After the survivors took to the boats her master, Captain Davies, was ordered on board the *U 66*. It safely returned to Europe where Captain Davies was sent to a prisoner of war camp.
The owners of the 'Saints' had started in

shipowning as recently as 1926, when George Bailey and Richard Street had independently formed tramp shipping companies, coming together to create B and S Shipping Co. Ltd. in 1933. The Government's Scrap and Build scheme provided the impetus for them to order an initial three ships from Thompsons as a nucleus of a liner service to South America. By 1939 sailings at ten-day intervals had been established, and the title of the

company owning several of the ships, including the *St. Clears* (lower photograph), was changed to the South American Saint Line Ltd.

St. Clears had her original White engine replaced in 1947 with what appears to have been an almost identical unit manufactured in 1944. This was destined to be the last of this type of machinery in service, surviving until 1962. *[Both: A. Duncan]*

E. and R. Management Co. Ltd. was formed by members of the Evans and Reid family in 1930, and initially bought second-hand tramps which they gave names beginning

Nailsea. Vessels were owned by the Bantham Steamship Co. Ltd. and the Nailsea Steamship Co. Ltd. E. and R. were quick to take advantage of the Scrap and Build

scheme, buying obsolete tonnage which they traded in against loans for the four White-engined tramps built by Bartrams. This is the first of the quartet, *Nailsea Court.*

6. NAILSEA COURT
O.N. 162113   4,946g 2,914n   420.3 x 56.0 x 25.4 feet
C. 4-cyl. by White's Marine Engineering Co. Ltd., Hebburn-on-Tyne with low-pressure turbine; 360 NHP, 1,562 IHP, 1,730 BHP, 10 knots.
9.6.1936: Launched by Bartram and Sons Ltd., Sunderland (Yard No. 272).
12.8.1936: Registered in the ownership of Bantham Steamship Co. Ltd. (E.R. Management Co. Ltd., managers), Cardiff as NAILSEA COURT.
10.3.1943: Torpedoed by the German submarine U 229 300 miles north west of Rockall in position 58.45 north by 21.75 west whilst on a voyage in convoy SC 121 from Beira, Table Bay and New York to London with general cargo including copper, nickel ore and asbestos. Of the 37 crew, 34 were lost plus the 2 passengers and 9 gunners.
23.8.1943: Register closed.

7. LLANASHE
O.N. 165338   4,836g 2,911n   432.7 o.a. 417.8 x 56.6 x 25.1 feet
C. 4-cyl. by White's Marine Engineering Co. Ltd., Hebburn-on-Tyne with low-pressure turbine; 348 NHP, 1,750 IHP, 10½ knots.
31.9.1936: Launched by Bartram and Sons Ltd., Sunderland (Yard No. 273).
18.11.1936: Registered in the ownership of the Clarissa Radcliffe Steam Ship Co. Ltd. (Evan Thomas, Radcliffe and Co., managers), Cardiff as LLANASHE.
17.2.1943: Torpedoed by the German submarine U 182 in position 34.22 south by 24.54 east whilst on a voyage from New York, Busreh and Bandar Abbas to Port Elizabeth and Table Bay with a cargo of tinplate and aluminium. 25 of the 35 crew and 3 of the 6 gunners were lost
23.3.1943: Register closed.

Cardiff's Evan Thomas, Radcliffe and Co. ordered two White-engined ships, and was obviously impressed enough to

acquire two more during and after the war, the *Biddlestone* and *Nailsea Moor.* The first to be delivered, *Llanashe*, cost

them £79,979 in November 1936. *[John B. Hill collection]*

8. NAILSEA MEADOW

O.N. 162118 4,962g 2,943n 420.3 x 56.0 x 25.4
C. 4-cyl. by White's Marine Engineering Co. Ltd., Hebburn-on-Tyne with low-pressure turbine; 348 NHP, 1,760 IHP, 10 knots.
18.12.1936: Launched by Bartram and Sons Ltd., Sunderland (Yard No. 274).
19.2.1937: Registered in the ownership of the Bantham Steamship Co. Ltd. (E.R. Management Co. Ltd., managers), Cardiff as NAILSEA MEADOW.
21.1.1941: Owners became the Nailsea Steamship Co. Ltd. (E.R. Management Co. Ltd., managers), Cardiff.
11.5.1943: Torpedoed by the German submarine U 196 off East London in position 32.04 south by 29.13 east whilst on a voyage from Hampton Roads, New York, Trinidad, Bahia, Rio de Janeiro and Table Bay to Durban, Bombay and Karachi with general cargo including war materials and mails. Of the crew of 37 plus 9 gunners, 2 members of the crew were lost.
11.8.1943: Register closed.

9. LLANDAFF

O.N. 165463 4,825g 2,902n 432.7 x 56.6 x 25.1 feet
C. 4-cyl. by White's Marine Engineering Co. Ltd., Hebburn-on-Tyne with low-pressure turbine; 348 NHP, 1,750 IHP, 10 knots.
17.3.1937: Launched by Bartram and Sons Ltd., Sunderland (Yard No. 275).

19.5.1937: Registered in the ownership of the Wimborne Steam Ship Co. Ltd. (Evan Thomas, Radcliffe and Co., managers), Cardiff as LLANDAFF.
1.10.1951: Sold to Robert Bornhofen, Hamburg, Germany and renamed MAX BORNHOFEN.
1952: Owners became Robert Bornhofen Reederi, Hamburg.
12.1958: Sold to the Anastasias Compania Ltda., San José, Costa Rica (Emmanuel A. Karavias) (Nomikos London Ltd., London, managers) and renamed ANASTASSIOS under the Greek flag.
20.2.1959: Grounded near Esbjerg after an engine breakdown during a voyage from Aalborg to Jeddah with a cargo of cement.
7.3.1959: Refloated but subsequently declared a constructive total loss.
10.7.1959: Arrived in tow at Ghent for breaking up by Van Heyghen Frères.

Nailsea Meadow light, probably on trials (upper). She carries a funnel design different to that used on the other three Nailsea vessels. *[World Ship Photo Library]*

Evan Thomas, Radcliffe's second White-engined ship, *Llandaff*, delivered in May 1937 for £80,542. *Llandaff* was distinguished as the only White-engined vessel to survive the war which kept its original machinery for all of her 'natural' life. *[National Museums and Galleries of Wales 1461/1556]*

10. BIDDLESTONE

O.N. 161606 4,910g 2,953n 414.8 o.a. 401.9 x 53.9 x 26.6 feet
C. 4-cyl. by White's Marine Engineering Co. Ltd.,
Hebburn-on-Tyne with low-pressure turbine; 348 NHP,
1,660 IHP, 10 knots.
10.5.1937: Launched by Short Brothers Ltd., Sunderland
(Yard No. 450).
7.1937: Completed.
5.7.1937: Registered in the ownership of the White
Shipping Co. Ltd. (Robert I. James, manager), Hebburn-on-
Tyne as BIDDLESTONE.
21.5.1940: Sold to the Clarissa Radcliffe Steamship Co.
Ltd. (Evan Thomas, Radcliffe and Co., managers), Cardiff.
27.7.1940: Renamed LLANCARVAN.
30.5.1943: Sunk by aircraft 160° and two miles off Cape St.
Vincent whilst on a voyage from Lisbon to Gibraltar with a
cargo of coal. All 46 crew and three passengers were saved.
10.7.1943: Register closed.

White's efforts to demonstrate his new engine by fitting it to a new
cargo ship built by Short Brothers were somewhat overtaken by
events, as by the time *Biddlestone* was delivered in July 1937 no
fewer than nine other ships with his machinery were in service.
[John B. Hill collection]

11. NAILSEA MOOR

O.N. 162123 4,926g 2,948n 420.3 x 56.0 x 25.4 feet
C. 4-cyl. by White's Marine Engineering Co. Ltd., Hebburn-on-
Tyne with low-pressure turbine; 348 NHP, 1,750 IHP, 10 knots.
1955: T. 3-cyl. made in 1950 by Harima Zosensho, Aioi, Japan.
12.6.1937: Launched by Bartram and Sons Ltd.,
Sunderland (Yard No. 276).
10.9.1937: Registered in the ownership of the Nailsea
Steamship Co. Ltd. (E.R. Management Co. Ltd.,
managers), Cardiff as NAILSEA MOOR.
15.5.1948: Sold to the Wynnstay Steamship Co. Ltd. and
W.I. Radcliffe Steamship Co. Ltd. (E.R. Management Co.
Ltd., managers), Cardiff.
11.6.1949: Renamed LLANWERN.
1950: Managers became Evan Thomas, Radcliffe and Co.,
Cardiff.
1951: Sold to Inui Kisen K.K., Kobe, Japan and renamed
KENNKON MARU.
1961: Sold to Yamato Gyogyo K.K., Chiba-ken, Japan, converted
into a fish factory ship and renamed FUJISAN MARU.
1964: Sold to Nikon Kokai Gyogyo K.K., Tokyo, Japan and
renamed RENSHIN MARU.
11.1968: Sold to Taiwan breakers.
13.3.1969: Breaking up began at Kaohsiung.

Nailsea Moor (below) was the only one of
the Nailsea quartet to survive the war. In
1947 her managers, E. and R. Management,
achieved the coup of acquiring the larger
and well-established Evan, Thomas
Radcliffe and Co. The yellow E. and R.
funnel with its blue band and gold feathers
was adopted by the ships of the older
company, much despised by the former
Evan Thomas, Radcliffe staff who dubbed
the company 'the Cardiff boy scout line.'
Although the funnel remained in use until
the firm ceased shipowning in the 1980s,
the name Evan Thomas, Radcliffe quickly
reappeared as the title of the ships'
managers.

Nailsea Moor's engines gave a
modest 18 years' service before being
replaced by conventional triple-expansion
machinery. *[World Ship Photo Library]*

Nailsea Manor [World Ship Photo Library]

12. NAILSEA MANOR
O.N. 162126 4,926g 2,946n 420.3 x 56.0 x 25.4 feet.
C. 4-cyl. by White's Marine Engineering Co. Ltd., Hebburn-on-Tyne with low-pressure turbine; 348 NHP, 1,750 IHP, 10 knots.
21.9.1937: Launched by Bartram and Sons Ltd., Sunderland (Yard No. 277).
6.12.1937: Registered in the ownership of the Nailsea Steamship Co. Ltd. (E.R. Management Co. Ltd. managers), Cardiff as NAILSEA MANOR.
10.10.1941: Torpedoed by the German submarine U 126 off the Cape Verde Islands in position 18.45 north by 21.18 west whilst on a voyage from Penarth to Freetown and Suez with a cargo of stores. The 36 crew and 5 gunners were saved.
22.12.1941: Register closed.

13. ST. ROSARIO
O.N. 162145 4,312g 2,602n 397.4 x 56.0 x 22.3 feet
C. 4-cyl. by White's Marine Engineering Co. Ltd., Hebburn-on-Tyne with low-pressure turbine; 304 NHP, 1,650 IHP, 1,475 BHP, 10¼ knots.
3.1958: Oil engine 2SCSA 6-cyl. by Nydqvist & Holm A/B, Trollhättan, Sweden.

22.9.1937: Launched by J.L. Thompson and Sons Ltd., Sunderland (Yard No. 582)
12.1937: Completed.
7.12.1937: Registered in the ownership of the Barry Shipping Co. Ltd. (B. and S. Shipping Co. Ltd., managers), Newport as ST. ROSARIO.
4.4.1939: Owners became the South American Saint Line Ltd. (B. and S. Shipping Co. Ltd., managers), Newport.
1952: Sold to Otto Bancks Rederi-A/B (Percy Banck), Helsingborg, Sweden and renamed KATIA.
1958: Renamed KATIA BANCK.
1965: Sold to Ypermachos Compania Naviera S.A., Panama (G. Lemos Brothers Co. Ltd., London, managers) and renamed YPERMACHOS under the Greek flag.
1968: Managers became Transatlantic Seaways Ltd. (N. Papathomas), London.
3.8.1969: Delivered to Chinese mainland shipbreakers for demolition at Whampoa.

A number of improvements were incorporated in the second batch of ships for B. and S. Shipping Co. Ltd., the most apparent being changes to the midships structure. This is *St. Rosario*, named in honour of Argentina's second largest city. [A. Duncan]

14. AGIOS GEORGIOS IV

4,847g 2,916n 431.3 x 56.6 x 24.8 feet
C. 4-cyl. by White's Marine Engineering Co. Ltd.,
Hebburn-on-Tyne with low-pressure turbine; 345 NHP.
14.4.1938: Launched by Bartram and Sons Ltd.,
Sunderland (Yard No. 279).
7.1938: Completed for N.G. Nicolaou (G. Nicolau (Hellas)
Ltd., managers), Piraeus, Greece as AGIOS GEORGIOS
IV.
8.6.1942: Sunk by gunfire from the Japanese submarine I-
16 off Madagascar in position 16.12 south by 41.00 east
whilst on a voyage from Suez and Aden to Table Bay and
eastern Canada in ballast. Seven of the 29 crew were lost.

Agios Georgios IV on trials, 21st September 1939.
(upper). *[National Maritime Museum P8646]*

St. Elwyn (lower) was the last of the White-
engined ships built, and also the shortest lived,
torpedoed with heavy loss of life during
November 1940. *[John B. Hill collection]*

15. ST. ELWYN

O.N. 162147 4,940g 2,937n 431.8 o.a. 415.1 x 58.2 x 24.8 feet
C. 4-cyl. by White's Marine Engineering Co. Ltd.,
Hebburn-on-Tyne with low-pressure turbine; 320 NHP.
17.8.1938: Launched by J.L. Thompson and Sons Ltd.,
Sunderland (Yard No. 589).
10.1938: Completed.
27.10.1938: Registered in the ownership of the Barry
Shipping Co. Ltd. (B. and S. Shipping Co. Ltd., managers),
Newport as ST. ELWYN.
4.4.1939: Owners became the South American Saint Line
Ltd. (B. and S. Shipping Co. Ltd., managers), Newport.
28.11.1940: Torpedoed by the German submarine U 103
500 miles west of the Bishop Rock in position 55.30 north
by 19.30 west whilst on a voyage from Hull to Santos with
a cargo of coal. Of the crew of 40, 29 were lost, the
survivors being picked up by the steamer LEEDS CITY
(4,758/1927) after several days in an open boat.
1.1.1941: Register closed.

INDEX TO RECORD 13 TO 16

Record 12: pp.1-64; *Record 13:* pp.65-128, *Record 14:* 129-192; *Record 15:* 193-264.

Index of articles

Index of ships

Llanashe: see page 256. *[National Museums and Galleries of Wales 80/296]*